Foraging

Tales from a Decade of Beekeeping Across the Globe

by

William Blomstedt

Wicwas Press LLC

Copyright © 2018 William Blomstedt

Photos and maps provided by the author

ISBN: 978-1-878075-51-2

Published by Wicwas Press LLC, 1620 Miller Rd., Kalamazoo MI 49001 USA

Parts of "Texas Ropes" and "Texas Lost" appeared as "Dead Cat Blues" in *Ambit*, issue 217, 2014.

"Turkey Quest" previously appeared as "The Quest for Anzer Honey— An Unguided Honey-Tasting Tour Through Eastern Turkey" in the *American Bee Journal*, vol. 151, no.2, February 2011, pp. 169-175.

A form of "Texas Flip" previously appeared as "Commercial Keeping" in *Safe to Chew: An Anthology*. Eds. Lawrence Connor, Randy Kim, Robert Muir. Wicwas Press, Kalamazoo, Mi. 2015.

A form of "Japan WOW" previously appeared as "Urban Beekeeping in Tokyo—Gucci Bees—The Ginza Beehive Project" in the *American Bee Journal*, vol. 153, no. 1, January 2013, pp. 47-50.

A form of "Australia Beeline" previously appeared as "The Buzz Down Under—Part III—*Apis cerana* and the Transition to Management Program" in the *American Bee Journal*, vol. 153, no. 5, May 2013, pp. 523-527

Parts of "China Pollination" previous appeared as "A Curious Bee-keeper Travels Through China—Part IV—Pollination by Hand and Bee in the *American Bee Journal*, vol. 153, no. 12, December 2013, pp. 1281-1284.

A form of "Slovenia Relations" previously appeared as "How to Become a Beekeeper (The Not-so-Straightforward Way): Part II—Conclusion" in the *American Bee Journal*, vol. 156, no. 5, pp. 553-556.

To my parents, for their endless support and encouragement

Bees

The Hive

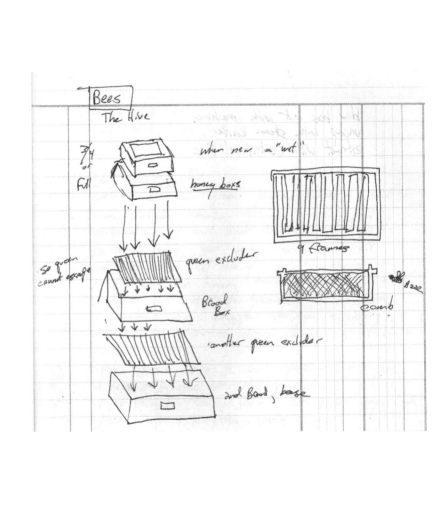

3/4
or
full

when new a "wet"

honey boxs

9 frames

So queen
cannot escape

queen excluder

Brood
Box

comb   B zzz

another queen excluder

2nd Brood, base

Contents

1

Jordan Overture

2009

γ

"Why don't you write an article for the *American Bee Journal?*"

These words, suggested by a Jordanian bee researcher named Nizar Haddad, kicked off my writing career. It was the January after my first season of working for a commercial beekeeper, and my high school friend Ryan and I had traveled to Jordan to visit his mom and step-dad. A season in the trenches of the bee industry had solidified my interest in the field, and I was ready to take a step further. One source of inspiration was Eva Crane's *A World History of Beekeeping and Honey-Hunting*, a 682-page tome that I consumed at night while my ears were still ringing from the buzz of the day's work in the hives.

Eva Crane was a fascinating woman: born in 1912, she trained to be a quantum mathematician but changed her field of study to honey bees, founded the International Bee Research Association, wrote over 180 scientific papers, and traveled to more than sixty countries—all in search of apicultural knowledge. This textbook on the history of bee-keeping practices, which she wrote and compiled when she was in her eighties, was the sum of her life's work. She passed away in 2007, aged ninety-five, just as my fascination with bees was blossoming.

By then I already had a budding case of "itchy feet" thanks to various family vacations during my youth. My parents had taken my sis-ter and I horse-packing in the Canadian Rockies, mountain biking in the Southwest, and bird-watching in Belize, to name a few. I honestly can't say how much I cared about these trips at the time, but the experiences must have instilled a curiosity of unfamiliar sights and tastes that fully cracked open just as I reached adulthood. Crane's story was hugely inspirational in seeing how I could possibly combine my interests while also trying to make an impact on the field. Somehow, I thought to myself while paging through it, I wanted to take up this torch. While on my trip to Jordan with Ryan, I looked up bee researchers and emailed Nizar out of the blue to ask if we could meet.

But for what? To learn about beekeeping in the desert? Other than that, my goal was vague. One cloudy morning I left Ryan and his family to traverse the city of Amman on my own. I boarded a crowded public bus, uncertain if it was the right line, and later took a cab which may have spun me in a few extra circles to pad the fare. Eventually, I arrived at the National Agricultural Research Center and wandered around the building until I saw posters of honey bees with Arabic script scrawled underneath. In a nearby office, Nizar sat behind his desk sporting a trim mustache and argyle sweater. He was discussing something with a graduate student—the title of her doctoral thesis, it turned out—and I was ushered to a chair while he finished the conversation. After she left, we began talking about bees, his research, and about beekeeping practices in Jordan, but I was at a loss to say what my true purpose was.

Until the moment he asked me if I was interested in crafting an article, writing outside of school assignments had never crossed my mind. I actually thought I was a mediocre writer (and today still struggle with every sentence), but I decided to give it a shot. My mother is a talented author, with many essays and one amazing memoir under her name, and I hoped a little of her ability had passed down to me.

A week later, I met Nizar once again for a more in-depth interview and a tour of the Center's Bee Research Unit. I did my best to emulate a real journalist, and, over the course of a morning, we covered a lot of ground; Nizar's gold medal from Apimondia, the country's native bee species (*Apis syriaca*), beekeeping courses the country offered for Iraqi refugees, problems with adulterated honey, and the nation's most recent surprise, the appearance of *Apis florea*, a non-native dwarf honey bee. In between the bee talk, we dove into other topics—

religion, climate, Middle Eastern politics—and I couldn't help but be amazed when, over a cup of tea, a pair of agricultural extension workers explained to me the influence of T.S. Eliot's *The Wasteland* on Arabic literature. Though bees were what brought me here, I thought to myself, this conversation is just as interesting.

When I returned to the US, I sat down with my notes, wrote the piece over the course of a week, and submitted it to the *American Bee Journal* (*ABJ*). To my intense surprise, I received an email the following day from Joe Graham, the magazine's editor, who praised the article. He said it would be published the following month.

And so began my career as a part-time writer. Over the past decade I worked for large and small commercial beekeeping operations—primarily those who produced and sold queen bees. Between working seasons, which lasted six to nine months, I traveled to new countries, visited friends in far-off places, and often played it by ear, not sure where the next job or opportunity would come from. Writing became a useful tool to supplement these off-season travels, often giving them a firmer purpose. Both skills allowed me to go to places and meet people I would not have encountered otherwise.

I was never trained in journalism, meaning I was mostly improvising my way through these pieces, but I tried to mask this lack of expertise with confidence and supplemented it with a healthy dose of curiosity. Over this period I wrote perhaps 70 bee-related articles while traveling through 50 countries. While the *ABJ* articles were mostly instructional or informational, the stories in this collection cover different ground. A few common themes pull through: the small moments inside the life of a beekeeper, the grinding, hard work involved in commercial apiculture, and a handful of sometimes foolish bee-related escapades I fell into while pursuing this passion.

A Danish bee extension officer named Flemming once said to me, "When I visit beekeepers in a different country, I don't care how the bees look. Open a hive anywhere, and it's basically the same. When I travel, I want to see how the beekeepers live." That sentiment really spoke to me. Beekeeping is a skill that allows a connection with other beekeepers, even if you don't speak the same language. Beekeeping can act as a language all in its own. I also think people in this field tend to be more introverted than most—they enjoy spending time in nature with their bees—but they are often willing to open up to talk about this subject that they love.

Honey bees seem to have a natural calling for the romantics. Virgil wrote about bees extensively millennia ago, and bees have found their way into the works of Rumi, Aristotle, Shakespeare, Tolstoy, Dickinson, Frost, Whitman, and so on. Has anyone waxed as eloquently about sheep or cattle? While there are many farmers who grow crops or raise animals in the world, I believe it takes a special kind of mindset to become a beekeeper—an individual who decided to care for a group of animals—insects no less—who, in the wrong moment, could rise up and collectively sting their caretaker to death. But the outcome of this wonderfully peculiar relationship provides us with ecosystem balance and health, a substance that seems to be taken straight from the heavens, and endless fascination. This series of stories celebrates those who pursue this passion.

2

New Zealand Ardor

2005

I stood among ten thousand flying bees and did not suffer a single sting. With my eyes closed, my arms held slightly away from my body and my palms up, I focused on the bees' presence in the surrounding air. The texture of the buzz was deep and dimensional as the bees bumped into my hands, shoulders, and chest. That I could open a hive—tearing off the roof of the bees' home, exposing them to light and air—and they didn't immediately attack in full force was, to me, a gut-punch of amazement. That I could lever out a comb and hold it aloft as most of the bees continued caring for larvae, cleaning cells, and eating honey, was a sign of the gods at work.

"Take these two as well," Keith, the owner of this beekeeping operation and my new boss, shouted from across the yard, breaking my reverie. He spoke kindly, even though I, his new helper, was standing idle at the height of a busy morning. He had probably seen reactions like mine before, and I suspected he had seen worse. Stepping into a storm of bees for the first time, even if fully protected with coveralls, leather gloves, and a bee-veil, is certain to draw an emotional reaction. It requires battling a deep-seated instinctual fear, staying calm while feeling surrounded, and learning how to trust a group of insects that mean no harm. The worst-case scenario is when the novice runs away screaming, never to be seen again.

I quick-stepped to where Keith had placed a few supers—boxes of honey—on their sides. Full of white-capped honeycomb, the supers were as heavy as rocks and strangely empty of bees. Each box was the collective effort of a hive gathering energy from the summer blossoms to power them through the winter dearth. Keith cracked open a propolis-sealed lid with his hive tool, and I suddenly had a front row seat to an alien world; the bees crawled across a maze of orchid-white burr comb while in between the frames a dark mass of activity continued to churn. The burr comb's split wax displayed hexagonal pots of gold that glinted in the sun, with the exposed honey quickly ceding to gravity and oozing downwards in thick droplets. The nearby bees, distracted from their current task, turned to the loose treasure and began to taste the stream with their tiny proboscises. They stood in a line, lapping, fixing the damage we had just done. When we closed the hive, they would build it all back up again.

It was my first day of beekeeping.

Two years earlier during the summer before my freshman year of college, I had worked on a grizzly bear population study in Montana. The job required hiking off-trail ten hours a day, nine days in a row, in the rugged and remote Bob Marshall wilderness area. Every day, we hauled around eighty pounds of gear including rolls of barbwire and multiple liters of "bear lure"—a toxic brew of fermented cow's blood and fish guts that required a long scrub if a drop of it got on your skin or clothing. Over the summer I had to spend a few episodes scouring my hand in an ice-cold mountain stream as dusk crept in, wondering if this stuff would lure a bear into my tent rather than into the non-invasive trap we had set a few miles away. We worked in two-person crews, and I spent all my days and around fifty nights in a tiny, stinky tent with Mark, a 42-year-old boat captain and recovering alcoholic who had recently been minted a wildlife biology undergraduate. He had an unbelievable cache of hilarious and harrowing stories from his wild youth, of winters spent tracking wolves in Yellowstone National Park, and journeys around the world. On my days off I hung out with the other crews—a ragtag bunch of adventurers who had covered every continent. When the summer season ended, most of them went on to the next amazing job—trapping wolverines in Canada, big cat research in Tanzania, salmon fishing in Alaska—while I drove back east to watch professors drone on about "society and place" and scratch big, meaningless terms on the white board.

Many of my bear co-workers had spoken rapturously about New Zealand—the mountains, the sea, the parks, the people, the diversity—and those stories played through my head as I crunched through the snow from auditorium to dorm. It took a term and a half before I made a decision: I would take the next year off from school to travel and work in New Zealand.

A year passed before I faced down the first major unstructured solo trip of my life. How do I pack for six months? How do I pack for six months when I had to carry everything on my back? Half of what I had spread out on my bed had to be put back in drawers, and even after that my backpack was overstuffed and heavy. Two pairs of pants, two shorts, four t-shirts, a handful of underwear and socks, a rain jacket, what else? A sweater. Would it be cold in the mountains? Two sweaters. A pair of sandals along with the hiking boots I would wear on the plane. Toothbrush, paste, band-aids, sunscreen, a few more odds and ends. My good luck statue of a laughing Buddha. Two books—*Cannery Row* by Steinbeck and *Hell's Angles* by H.S. Thompson—as well as my portable CD player and five CDs—just like I was heading to a desert island. My first lesson in minimalism was taught by a rucksack.

After an eighteen-hour plane ride, I immediately boarded a bus which took me five hours north of Christchurch. Through a very distant contact I had arranged a gig on a sheep, cattle, and deer ranch. When I finally arrived, severely jetlagged and only a mere hour after setting down my backpack, the lady of the ranch handed me a rifle, walked me into the hills, and I shot my first wild pig. I carried the body back to the house and then learned how to dress a dead animal. As we dined on sweet-and-sour pork later that evening, I was shocked to learn that the lady with whom I went hunting and who cooked the meal was a vegetarian. By the end of the meal as I got to know my new hosts, the knot of worry began to unfold inside me. The first day of my solo trip on the opposite side of the world ended in oddity dovetailed with comfort and kindness. The adventure ahead began to take shape, and the future looked bright.

I stayed on the ranch for a few weeks, proudly perfecting the art of keeping a mug of tea level while riding in a truck along a rutted dirt track, but then it was time to move on. I began floating around the South Island looking for the next thing. On a whim, I cold-called a beekeeper who told me he could use some help harvesting honey. That's when I met Keith. Two days later, I was thrust into the life of full-on beekeeping.

I was completely amazed by this relationship. Here we had Man working with Insect to create Honey: an ambrosial concoction of dehydrated plant juices that brightens our taste buds and enlivens our food. Honey is the sweetness pulled from the land and distilled into a viscous substance. If you have a hive of bees in your backyard, they will fly up to three miles from your house to collect nectar. Put a spoon of that honey in your mouth, and you will be able to read the surrounding landscape like a book: the early spring dandelions, a neighbor's flower garden, the summer clover. It causes one to be aware of their surroundings—whether they be good or bad—and, in either case, how to improve them.

While making this honey, bees unknowingly provide an essential service to many of our food crops and the greater ecosystem: that of transferring pollen from one flower to another. This causes the flower to create a fruit which then falls to the ground and is the seed of a new plant: the art of reproduction. Over millennia, plants evolved nectar production to attract pollinators which would aid them in this process. When we humans stepped in the picture, we found that one of these outputs—honey—was extremely delicious, and, over time, we transformed from being pure predators to understanding there was a way to join this reciprocal relationship. Today, those carrying the torch that bridges the human-insect world are beekeepers. These thoughts bubbled through my head that first morning of work as I walked among the bees, carrying heavy boxes of honey, and tying them down.

As we worked, Keith taught me the basics of bee biology. I learned about the three types of bees and the structure of the colony: first, there is the queen who is the mother of all bees in the hive. Then, there are workers who are all female, make up approximately ninety percent of the population, and perform all the hive's tasks. Finally, there are the male drones whose job was to mate with other queens.

Inside one hive, I watched one queen insert her abdomen into a cell and lay an egg. The egg looked like a tiny grain of rice, and across a single comb I could see its future. A few cells away, older eggs had transformed into larvae, multiplying their weight some two thousand times in six days before being capped with wax for pupation. There the larva undergoes an amazing metabolic transformation, and in two more weeks, a fully formed worker bee would climb out of that cell, waxy-pale and new to the world.

This bee's life follows a general progression of tasks. Starting as a cell cleaner, she then moves onto duties such as nursing, wax production, queen care, honeycomb building, guard duty, and, finally, forager. I was astounded to learn that during summer, this life-span only amounted to a matter of weeks. Foragers fly until their wings wear out or they are eaten by a predator, and they are quickly replaced by members of a younger cohort who themselves are replaced by workers from one step lower, and so on, sending the hive's wheel spinning straight back to the queen (and the drones who fertilized her), who will lay more than her bodyweight in eggs in a day, and in a single season produce 200,000 bees.

Once we had taken the supers from every hive and the truck was stacked high, we returned to Keith's property—his honey house was a converted garage next to his real house. Here, I learned how to extract honey from the comb: cutting the beeswax cappings with a steam knife, loading the frames in the centrifugal extractor, and then letting it spin the honey out of them.

With the machine cranked up to full speed and shuddering like an amusement park ride gone haywire, I peered over the rim of the extractor and watched the drops of honey fling against the walls of the metal drum, slide downwards, and collect in the sump below along with fragments of wax and insect parts. Then, the honey was put through a filter and pumped a beautiful golden-brown stream into a nearby tank. As we cut the caps and handled the full and empty frames, my hands acquired a sticky-sweet honey sheen, and I couldn't help but sneak a lick every now and then. On one wall of the extracting room hung a poster of Sir Edmond Hillary, a fellow Kiwi, who credited the experience of working in his family's beekeeping business as a foundation of the durability and character which eventually led him to be the first of two to climb Mount Everest. Damn cool, I thought.

After breaking for lunch my day was done. My deal with Keith was that I would get room and board in return for a half-day of labor—essentially WWOOFing[1]. In the afternoons I took the '86 mud-brown hatchback I had bought for $400 and explored the beautiful New Zealand countryside for hikes and swimming holes. In the evenings, after joining the family for dinner, I would retire to my tiny trailer in the front yard and pored through Keith's bee books by headlamp. I filled my notebook with notes about bee biology, beekeeping methods, sketches of equipment, and questions I could ask Keith.

The days passed in a beautiful harmony. From my admittedly brief and superficial view, Keith seemed to have a great life. An Englishman, he had drifted to New Zealand twenty years earlier and bought this small farm from a guy he described as a "stoned hippie". He married a Canadian—Nancy Jean—then began keeping bees, and his operation grew to about four hundred hives. His main crop was Manuka honey, which had just burst onto the international health scene as "the" healthy honey and could be sold at a premium price. He was his own boss and he lived in a beautiful and rural place with his wife, two daughters, and an incredibly smart dog named Milo whom I loved dearly and would often take with me on my afternoon explorations. Those few weeks laid some groundwork for the future life I one day wanted to lead.

I woke up each morning excited about what I would learn and ready to push my body into the hard, physical tasks that needed to be done. New and fascinating facts arrived at every hour; bees hate dark colors like black and brown, which are frequently the dressing of their predators, but they also dislike red because to them it looks like the color black. Instead, they can see ultraviolet, or "bee purple", because their vision is shifted along the color spectrum, and a certain flower that is plain white to us may have an extensive and beautiful ultraviolet pattern to a bee. After a scout bee finds these flowers, she will return to the hive to "dance" for other foragers who understand that the length and angle of the dance indicates the distance and direction they should fly, while the enthusiasm or vigor of the dance indicates the quality of the patch.

Between these facts and lessons on basic beekeeping—how to use smoke to calm the colony or how to properly remove a comb from

[1]Willing Workers on Organic Farms—a worldwide program that connects farmers and volunteer workers.

the hive without injuring or alarming the bees—Keith might use his hive tool to scrape off a chunk of honeycomb the size of a golf ball and point it at me. Though the air was thick with bees, a fresh piece of honeycomb was too tempting to pass up. I would loosen the strings of my veil and quickly slip the chunk of honey into my protected zone and then into my mouth. The explosion of sweetness and flavor would momentarily drown out every other sense, and I would soar across the fields hundreds of times with the bees who had gathered and distilled the landscape into that single bite.

Bouncing across rutted fields and cresting over a hill for a view of the ocean. The roar of the bees fanning at night, and the smell of fresh nectar filling the cool air. A pair of giant islands in the South Pacific home to three million people and eighty million sheep. I was here while on the other side of the world my fellow students were huddled in an extended February freeze, going through the motions of taking notes and hoping that the itch in the back of their throat wasn't turning into the flu. I rode in a truck with the windows rolled down and the landscape in a deep summer heat. I was wearing wellies that were too small. I was sweaty, dirty, and tired. But I was in love.

3

Texas Sweat

2008

❦

9 AM had not yet struck, and my t-shirt was already fully soaked with sweat.

If I had been wearing only a t-shirt, the Texan sun might have been manageable, but I had on much, much more. Over a pair of jeans and a long-sleeved collared shirt, I wore a thick but hole-strewn pair of coveralls, zipped to the neck with their legs tucked in ankle high boots. The boots were wounded as well: one showed the entirety of the steel toe, the other with a sole that began to flap and would soon fall off. On my hands I wore leather gauntlets, dark with grime and honey, patched together with strips of duct tape. When I got them a few short months earlier, they were lamb-white, soft as a babe, and slid on effortlessly. Over the stress of thousands of motions handling wooden hives, metal tools, and tying down rope, they cracked and tore, exposing certain parts of my hand to stings tens of times a day, giving me a permanent state of fat-knuckle. Yet they had not yet crossed the threshold of being so bad that I should buy a new pair of gloves, so every truck ride between yards included a few minutes of duct tape reinforcement. At night the gloves would solidify in their empty state to become bark-solid. The following morning I would have to spend a minute wriggling my hand inside each glove before they were once again malleable and allowed me any digital dexterity.

Five of us worked in the bee yard this morning, shaking packages. This meant identifying strong hives and taking excess bees from them, apportioning three pounds of bees into a small box with mesh sides and then adding a caged queen and a can of sugar syrup with a slow drip. This package would then be sold to a beekeeper somewhere in America, who could dump it into an empty hive, release the queen from her cage, and soon have a colony ready for the summer honey flow. Selling packages can be a great business for beekeepers—often more lucrative than producing honey and without having to truck the bees across the country for pollination rentals.

With the recent uptick in beekeeping interest, we had many novice customers who would order packages year after year as they slowly came to grips with the delicate apicultural equation: the difficulty in keeping bees alive, time spent on a hobby, cost of bees every year, and money already sunk into equipment. Unfortunately, the plethora of pests and diseases that fill the modern beehive means that beekeeping is no longer as easy as putting a single colony in the backyard and ignoring it until the honey harvest.

Packages are mainly produced in the southern US, where bees start their year much earlier, and producers can prepare and ship packages just as spring cracks open in the north. Early spring is the busy season for package producers and, as this was the time of my graduation, it was this area of the industry that sucked me in. I had the opportunity to go to Texas. Coming from the north, Texas had a not-too-bright reputation, but I was curious. Would Texas really be Texas? Oil men with cowboy hats? Bucking broncos? Friday Night Lights? Would I, like our fair, Connecticut-born president, quickly adopt a Texan accent? After I finished my last university exam, I packed my car and drove south. The next week, I was shaking packages.

Here are the steps in shaking a package: open a hive and analyze a few combs: are there eggs? Is there *STING* brood? Do the bees have enough food? Is the queen laying eggs in a nice pattern? Is there enough pollen? Is there any sign of disease? If something looks wrong, take *STING* action (add antibiotics, give sugar syrup, replace queen, add brood from another hive, add bees from another hive, reorganize *STING* the frames). If the hive is strong enough to spare bees, take the top super and *STING* put it on the shaker box—a wooden contraption with the dimensions of a hive and topped with a metal basket whose slats are large enough for worker bees to crawl through into a bottom box, but a queen bee, with her *STING* slightly larger abdomen, cannot. Bang the super violently five or six times *STING* so the bees *STING* fall into the *STING* OWWWW... basket. The basket is now a *STING* squirming mass of bees. Puff smoke on them so they crawl down through the mesh. Take a good look in the basket for the queen bee. If spotted, use *STING* your hive tool and hand to ferry her into the hive. Dump the remaining bees into the bottom of the box. Put the hive back together and move onto the next *STING* hive.

This was our chore for the day. Together we had to get one hundred twenty packages, or three hundred sixty pounds of bees, before we could call it quits. If the hives were strong, shaking this quantity of packages wouldn't be so bad. Five of us could go through three yards by the late afternoon and cover that number. But if the hives were weak, it meant going to a fourth yard and having the day stretch into the evening. In either case, it meant a lot of heaving boxes, sweating under the hot sun, and, of course, getting stung.

Our crew spent a lot of time together under these strenuous circumstances. Most often we would work while lost in weariness, with only the sounds of buzzing bees punctuated by the occasional, operational exchange ("Need a comb of brood over here"). But there were exceptions. Barry, the jokester, would rib at me every now and then ("I bet up north you thought 'Manual Labor' was the name of a Mexican guy"), take shots at the rest of the crew ("We got Tweedle-Dee and Tweedle-Plain-@#!$&-Stupid with us today), take on Texas itself ("You people fought Mexico for this? What, did your great-grandfather's horse die here?"), or would just open up a hive and yell ("Holy shit, this thing is full of bees! What the #!$@& are we going to do?"). Barry added some color to the otherwise functional and frustrated conversation, but the more colorful character to work with was Brian.

Brian was a through-and-through Texan. Graybearded, often with a ball-cap and suspicious look in his eye, he lived in a trailer next to the operation's honey house and acted as part-guard, part-handyman, who, as of earlier in the year, had never opened a hive of bees. But after a few quick coworker defections, we were suddenly short on staff, and Brian was coerced into becoming a beekeeper. One personal tidbit I remember Brian telling me soon after we met was that he shot his first gun when he was either four or five years old—he knew the year was 1967, but he didn't know what month.

As Brian began working out in the field, I realized that he didn't have a functioning internal monologue. Everything came out. Working next to him in the bee yard sounded something like this:

"OK. Now I'm gonna... let's see. I'm gonna take this box off and put it here. Now I'm gonna check for eggs. I'll take out a comb... oh. Woah, Nellie. Got a bee in my veil. How'd you get in there. Urg. You little @&!$#. Uh. You little @$#&-ing $%#. @!&#%. Shit $#@&-ing $%@#. How do you like that you little #!&%? $#!@ you. You wanna sting me? You do? Ow. &@!#. Ouch. You did. Ha. You stung me. Well guess what? You're gonna die now, huh. That's a shame. Too bad. Too. #%@!&. Bad. Really, that's a bummer. Woah, Nellie, another one. Little %#@!-ing !$&@#. *crunch* Got her. OK. Now, where was I? Right. I'll check for eggs..."

This monologue could last twenty minutes, an hour, the entire morning, and, working through hives a few feet away, it washed over me. I picked up the super and slammed it onto the shaker box. Thousands of bees tumbled into the basket, and I stared into the abyss of these writhing insects. All of these beings before my eyes, each with a little brain, legs and wings. I let my gaze wander around the basket until I saw the queen's abdomen poking out of a corner. It is amazing how the eye grows used to a pattern—at first it would take many minutes of searching for me to spot a queen, one slightly different insect out of thousands. But after months of practice, I could spot her like the apple in a pile of oranges. Later, at night, a movie of squirming bees would play across the backs of my eyelids as I drifted into sleep.

I finished one hive and moved onto the next. Bees stung me through my suit. Bees somehow snuck inside my clothing and crawled up my bare legs, on my back, into my damp armpits. I continued working as their wings tickled me. If I walked out of the yard to extract every bee from my suit, I would never get anything done, and if I tried to crush the interloper, 90% of the time she would sting me anyway. So, often I let her wander around my core until I bent over, the fabric pressing her against me, and she stung out of fear. The shock of pain was like a hot match head pressed against my skin, her venom injected into me, a small life being transferred into mine.

On my darker days, after going through a hundred hives and having a hundred more ahead of me, with all corners of my body smarting from stings and the bees banging into my veil like a snare drum, I'd have my own monologue running through my head: bees, you are no longer the fascinating and noble insects I imagined you to be. I wanted this job to feel connected to the land, to work while listening to the wind, to understand your ordered system of life, and to learn grace. Now, when I open a hive, I see you as just another item on the long factory belt which I look at, fix, and move onto the next. There is no time for wonder. This is business, and I am a cog in the works. A cog that is getting stung.

We finished the yard somewhere past 11 AM. The already cruel sun was still not the cruelest we would see that day, yet I still had probably lost a pound or two in liquid weight. For most of the yard, I had been day-dreaming of the frozen water bottle in my backpack—it was un-equivocally a bad day if I forgot to put in the freezer the night before and had to drink ditch-warm water—but when surrounded by defensive bees, even a sip of the coldest water was not worth the potential five stings to the face, and it had to wait. The yard was a weak one and we only had twenty-eight packages tied on the truck's bed. We loaded the rest of the equipment and tied it down while the bees continued to bombard us, searching for that final sting. Getting in the truck wasn't the end either—the most persistent guard bees followed us inside the cab, and we had to keep our gear on and the windows down as the truck bounced across the pasture. After passing through the gate, Barry gave the signal, and we rolled up the windows. With our gloves or empty cigarette boxes, we smashed the final half-dozen bees against the windows, their yellow guts joining the thousands of others crusted upon the glass, never to be cleaned. Then we were on the road, windows down, veil finally off, and sweet, blessed, cold water down the hatch, fostering my strength for the next round.

4

Texas Wisdom

2008

Afternoons with Binford were a joy. They were a sought-after break during the dreariness of shaking season, when the needed number of packages always seemed greater than the colony conditions would allow, and working afternoons would stretch into evenings with the next morning following very quickly after. But on odd days, for one reason or the other, Binford would need help with his queens, and I would be fortunate enough to spend an afternoon with him. Not only would the work be easier than the sweaty slog of cruising through yards with a shaker box, but it also meant a few hours of observing a beekeeping veteran and improving my skills.

Binford was eighty-two years old when I met him and already had a long and amazing beekeeping career under his belt: he had successfully run the family operation for many decades, was a pioneer in both migratory beekeeping and queen breeding in Hawaii, and had been president of the American Beekeeper's Foundation as well as recipient of their highest award. He had every right to kick back and relax in his old age, but he was still coming out to work with his bees daily. I, being a new beekeeper, thought it was a good sign to see a man of his age still showing up to this job. Eighty-two meant that Binford had something like seventy-odd years of experience working with bees, which was three times as long as I had been alive. Though I had heard that

Binford had a bit of fire in him as a younger man, he was a fairly mellow camper at this age, other than an occasional tantrum when he was confused why his brain and memory were not what they used to be.

Binford stood a little hunched over in his age, with kind eyes and large ears sticking outside a dollop of white hair. He liked to talk with his hands—they were always complementing or enhancing his words—and he'd clap them together at the start of the day as he told us the chores ahead. Binford worked on the queen breeding and cell production side of the operation. In actuality, this wing was run by Susan, a fierce, funny and efficient woman who spent half her time beekeeping in Texas and the other half working in Alaska, who drove that long road-trip twice a year. But Binford still came out every day to look at a few hives and make the big decisions, which Susan had to twist into line with the reality of eleven other smaller decisions and spend twelve hours of her day making them happen.

On these afternoons with Binford, he would drive us to one of the nearby yards while patting the steering wheel and humming a tune from his memory. After parking the truck, we would both light smokers and then begin to move through the hives; he would work on one side of a four-hive pallet, I on the other, keeping my eye on his conduct and trying to emulate how he moved around bees.

Incredibly, Binford didn't usually work with gloves. I would watch him lever out a full comb of bees in a thin, collared shirt with his wrists and knuckles exposed, while I, a few feet away, would be dressed like an astronaut. While his bees would be calm, my bumbling movements would incite the hive in front of me, causing them to attack Binford as well. "Baloney!" or "Sam Hill!" he'd curse in his thick Texan accent, phrases that I was both delighted to hear used in sincerity but embarrassed that I was the cause of them. Thus, Binford would keep an eye on my hive, telling me when I was handling it poorly or shooting a puff of smoke across the top bars at precisely the right moment. I often wondered, watching a guard shoot out and attach her stinger to his gnarled knuckle, how many bees had stung his hands over the course of his career. Thousands upon thousands. But he took each sting with barely a flinch, flicking out the stinger with little afterthought. Beekeepers, I came to realize, have a high tolerance for pain.

Through these sessions with Binford, I learned the importance of demeanor around bees. When opening a hive, if the beekeeper is relaxed, calm, and moves slowly, the bees will be easier to work with. I am sometimes asked if my bees can recognize me, and if they are friendlier to me than to strangers. It's not quite true. Bees understand body language. Quick and sharp movements will cause them to jump from their hive and sting, while composure will not bother them as much. With enough experience one can read a colony's mood in the same way that one can see a horse suddenly turn back its ears. Using the precise amount of smoke and the correct deportment, it is usually possible to work with bees comfortably without gloves.

Binford and I would slowly work through the yard, kneeling opposite each other, pulling out frames of bees and figuring out how to improve their state. I had to keep a close eye on both my smoker and hive tool during these sessions. Binford, when distracted, would pick up whichever tool was in his reach and move away with it, his own hive tool sticking out of his back pocket.

After closing the hive he'd just been working on, Binford would often leave something on the cover: either three rocks in a line, two on opposite corners, or, the classic, one rock dead in the center. This was a code for the next beekeeper who came through the yard. It could mean that the hive needed a new queen, that it just got a new queen, that it was diseased and needed attention, or that it was a potential breeder and could be the savior for the entire operation. Each rock arrangement certainly meant something when Binford placed it, but the problem was the meaning of these signs often fluctuated without warning. On one week, three rocks might mean the hive has a queen problem, but on the next it unintentionally morphs into a signal that the hive needs food. And if it was a stick on top of the hive instead of a rock, did that mean something different, or was it just that the yard didn't have any rocks? I was often confronted by these hieroglyphs of a previous inspection but could only sweep off the refuse and give the hive slightly more attention. I didn't feel too badly about being unable to interpret them because I would see Binford go through the same process: trying to remember what he had meant by this symbol the last time but knowing the only way to find out was to dig into that hive once again.

"Bees, bees, what do you do to me?" he would mutter, flipping over a comb. "Ah, there she is," he'd say, spying the queen like she was a firefly, even with his old eyes. Then, he'd show me her spotty brood pattern caused by European foulbrood—a common, bacterial disease that melts affected brood into puddles—and explain why this was the right time to replace her. I'd file that fact away in my brain and then pepper him with as many questions as I could muster as we worked down the line. I did notice that when we came back to the yard the following week, the hives he worked seemed to be in better shape than mine.

One vivid memory I have with Binford was when we had just received a few breeder queens from a research facility in Louisiana. Each little insect stalking about its cage cost over a thousand dollars. Instead of "free mating", where newly hatched queens go on mating flights and copulate with more than a dozen wild drones (any old riff-raff that was flying about), these queens had been bred for generations using artificial insemination, where a specialist with a tiny syringe and a steady hand milked drones with desired traits like high honey production or disease resistance, and then manually inseminated the queen. We would then use the larvae from these mothers to stock our own hives and sell the second generation queens to our customers.

I cradled the breeder queens in my lap as we drove to the yard which would be their new home. On the way, Binford decided we should carry some extra queens with us, and we stopped at the grafting yard to pick up a rack. As I looked through the queen banks, Binford didn't like the activity at one nearby hive's entrance and popped open the top. Something he saw inside—the hive arrangement, maybe—bothered him, so he took a few minutes to fix it and then looked in the next hive, and then opened a third to find more brood, and began explaining to me why all three of these hives were not performing very well.

The lesson continued into a fourth hive, then a fifth, and Binford was fuming at whoever had left these hives in such terrible shape. Unsure if I was the culprit, I continued watching and asking questions. Time slipped away, and when I glanced up I saw the truck was now in full sunshine.

"The queens!" I yelled and ran to the truck. I had parked in the shade, but the five-minute stop had stretched into forty-five minutes, and the summer Texan sun had shifted and turned the truck into a makeshift oven with thousand-dollar queens baking inside. I found the cages in the cup holder, each holding a curled up, motionless insect.

"Oh, no," Binford moaned. "Gosh, darn, tootin'." He tilted one cage and watched the husk of the queen tumble into the corner. I felt the weight of responsibility—while he was the elderly fount of wisdom, my main job was to be the working memory and stay on top of these small but important logistics. Queens and hives with blocked entrances always had to be in the shade. Anything left in this June sunlight would get fried.

Binford took the top off the nearest hive and flipped it upside-down. He opened the small cages one by one and dumped the motionless queens onto the wood. Then, he took a comb of bees from the queen bank and shook a small clump of bees next to them. The fallen bees gained their footing and then, attracted by the pheromones, gathered around the three queens and began to tend to them. Their short, pink proboscises worked over the queens' exoskeletons: the abdomens, legs, heads and antennae. Binford and I knelt next to the top and waited to see what happened. After 15 minutes, two of the queens began to flex their legs and creep back from the edge of the abyss. One remained curled on its side, forever lost in the depths.

5

Texas Ropes

2008

⸕

Another afternoon of shaking packages. Yard number three had just creaked into motion, and the thought of the day's end was starting to take shape. Each of us had on our own line of six pallets, four hives on each. This yard was rife with European foulbrood and hive beetles—a horrendous death-ladybug whose larva can transform a beehive into an empty slime pit. My phone rang as I put the lid on the first hive. With my glove still on I dug the phone out of my sticky pocket and held it close to my ear.

"Will," Binford drawled, giving my name an extra syllable. "We're gonna need you to move some bees this afternoon. You know Applegate?"

"Yep," I replied. It was a long drive away.

"They just called up and said they are going to spray something or whatever around there, so we need the hives moved before four today. Can you do that?"

"Sure. Where do they go?"

"Oil Pad. Do you know that yard?"

"No."

"Well, let's see. From Applegate you take a left, then drive three or four miles until you hit Route 63..."

"Hold on," I said and ran back to the truck. I knew from experience that I would remember the first few turns, but as they piled on (as they surely would) the later instructions would get pushed below the surface, and I'd be blindly lost. I found a marker and an old cookie package to write on.

Binford repeated the directions, and I scribbled down as much as I could. After finishing the call, I sat back against the seat and felt a lightness in my being. The rest of my day would be an easy bee move while my co-workers would be sweating their asses off here. I removed the remaining gear from the bed of the 2-ton Freightliner, drove back to the shop for the Bobcat trailer, and was soon on the road with the window down and radio playing loudly. The tail-end of the day looked bright.

We had dozens of yards in the operation, and my knowledge of each was relative to the number of times I visited them. Applegate was an easy yard to find. I actually knew where it was as a driver, as opposed to "knowing" as a passive passenger and suddenly discovering with the steering wheel in hand that all the turns looked the same. Getting to it required passing through a few gates, which is a pain when you are alone (opening, driving through, closing), but time was on my side. After arriving to the yard, I pulled up to the hives, turned off the truck, and watched the bees fly. They flowed out of their hives, circling, swooping, busy in search of local nectar. I ate my second sandwich of the day and drank some water which I was pleased to find still cold from spending the night in the freezer.

I lit my smoker and began to dress for the project ahead. First, I tucked the cuffs of my jeans into boots—there was nothing worse than the feeling of a bee crawling higher and higher on my bare leg, really not wanting it to sting me, but knowing that a decision was required. The higher it went, the more it would hurt. Then, I stepped into the jump suit, which at that point in the week (Wednesday) had acquired an unappealing, sticky brown-black color. By Saturday, the suit could nearly stand on its own, and each laundry cycle probably took weeks off the life of the washing machine. Next were the plastic pith helmet and fold-up metal veil which I tied in a specific but important way—strings around the back and through the loops once again so that the edge of the veil held tightly against my chest, preventing any curious and persistent bees from climbing inside. A further level of security could be achieved if the veil is donned before the suit, but I only used this technique on special, desperate occasions. Finally came the leather gauntlets, also brown-black, cinched by elastic above the elbows.

Fully protected, I walked through the yard, giving each hive four or five big puffs of smoke. The correct method of moving hives is to wait until the foragers return at dusk and the whole colony is inside. Then, each entrance should be blocked, the hives lifted onto the truck, tied down, covered in nets, tied down again, and then moved to the new location. But with the pressure of the busy season, when chores multiplied exponentially and already spilled into over-hours each day, some good practices got wiped off the chalkboard. No one wanted to give up their already-short free hours to move hives after sundown, so we often just left a single colony behind to collect the confused foragers who came back to find their hive missing. Also, if we kept the truck moving on back roads, there was arguably no need to take the extra time to throw a net over the hives. Bees don't like flying on a windy day. While some bees might jump out and be left along the road, driving at 40 MPH makes for an artificial windstorm that keeps most bees at home.

With the smoke calming the bees, I let down the legs of the Bobcat trailer, climbed into the machine, and lowered the safety bar. With the turn of the key, the engine roared to life. Pushing the levers forward, I wheeled down the ramp and onto the grass.

Sixteen pallets stood in two rows, each with two-to-four hives of varying height on them. Nearby, a pile of broken boxes and other junk lay on another pallet that I would take as well. While smoking the yard, I made sure there were enough pallets of three or four evenly-sized hives so they could act as a bottom row, and I could stack others on top of them.

The loading went smoothly. Usually, a bee move was a two-person task—one to work the Bobcat, the other to smoke the hives and tie them down—but it was possible to do on my own. The bees, confused and jostled, shot out of the hives and straight into my mask, but I was well protected and suffered only a minimal number of stings. I had become pretty comfortable handling pallets of beehives and even found fitting the pieces together on the back of the truck a fun puzzle. Soon, the hives were stacked neatly on the Freightliner's bed, and I backed the Bobcat onto the trailer. A cloud of bees sped to-and-fro above where their homes used to be, but they were no longer stinging. I looked upon the yard with the satisfaction of a job well done.

The sweetness of the moment came crashing down when I opened the truck's storage box and found it suspiciously empty. I looked everywhere—in the cab, the sleeper and the battery box—but the ropes were gone. Someone had committed one of the gravest sins of a beekeeping operation: taking the ropes from one truck without mentioning it or returning them. Here I was left holding the bag. These rope stealers would one day find themselves in a special circle of Hell, I thought, along with those who swipe a spare tire or a jack from another truck. Standing next to a flat tire in a rural field an hour away from the shop and realizing the truck's pumpjack had not been returned is truly a rage-inducing moment.

There were only two full ropes left in the storage box. After digging a bit, I found three smaller pieces of rope that I fashioned into a large one. I needed around eight ropes for a truly secure load, but 4 PM was fast approaching and no rope store was within walking distance. I could throw one rope over each pallet, and I could either toss the junk on the ground or keep it on the back untied. I thought the matter over while I tightened the trucker hitches. Drive slowly and gingerly, I reasoned with myself, and the junk will stay. I cursed the rope-stealer once again.

I started the engine, buckled my seatbelt, and spun the truck around in a big circle. Driving in the rutted path along the fence was smooth, but when I had to take a wide turn into the pasture to get a better angle at the gate, each and every bump seemed endlessly disruptive to my load. A pair of cows on the other side of the fence watched me get out and open the gate, their bovine minds wondering if I was bringing them lunch. I drove through the gate and three bothered bees stung me on the way back to the cab. One of the cows also suffered an attack, rearing and shaking its head. The bees were taking their displeasure out on any man or beast within reach.

With great care and a mind towards the laws of physics, I pulled the truck onto the asphalt road and brought it up to speed. The cookie wrapper with Binford's instructions pressed against the steering wheel. Go three or four miles and turn right onto Route 63. This was a junction with a traffic light, and as soon as I turned I felt a dark premonition in my stomach. This direction didn't feel right. But there was no turning back, and soon the road was as thin as a stream of piss, my lane squished without a shoulder between the oncoming traffic and a three-foot culvert on the right. I took shallow breaths so as not to nudge the wheel and send myself into either side. Houses began gathering along the road at an alarming rate. A few steeples poked through the air. Six glinting pickup trucks ran hot on my tail like they would happily drive me off the road just to get to the Dollar Store a minute faster. Looking ahead, I knew where this road was taking me.

"Oh, no, Binford." I muttered. As soon as was possible, I pulled onto a shoulder and let the trucks pass. One of them demonstrated his feelings with a middle finger stuck out his window. Binford's route would take me straight through Katy, a not insignificant city, and I was carrying a load of live, stinging insects, without nets, without being fully tied down, on a busy Wednesday afternoon. Driving with semi-secured beehives surreptitiously on country dirt roads was one thing, but taking them through an urban area was a potential catastrophe. Binford's mind was probably stuck in the 1960s when this road meandered through farms and fields. Now, the creeping oil-fed sprawl had transformed Katy into a long strip mall of car dealerships, Joe's Crab Shacks, and H-E-Bs that made it indistinguishable from any other mid-sized Texan town.

Not only was my load illegal and dangerous, but I was also driving the truck with a learner's permit. Technically, someone with a valid commercial driver's license (CDL) had to be in the passenger seat as I drove, but as the other guy with the CDL had quit two months earlier, necessity dictated that the rules be malleable. Like the road before me, perhaps Binford thought these sorts of licensing rules could be resolved with an old-fashioned Texan grin.

There was no choice but to go forward—and quickly; I was sitting in front of someone's house without the rushing wind, and the bees had begun leaving the hives looking for someone to sting. I pulled onto the narrow road and followed the directions: take a right onto a busy frontage road with multiple lanes. Here, I entered the heart of the beast.

Luckily, the sun was fierce, so everyone had their windows up with AC blasting, and the sidewalks were empty. Actually, there were no sidewalks in this town; who would want to walk when you could drive? Among the many cars around me, only my windows were down because the truck's AC blew air hotter than it was outside. Every light I approached seemed to turn red, and, while waiting, I peeked in the mirror and could see a handfuls of bees jumping into the air.

The song on the radio annoyed me, so I switched to another station out of Houston. Riding alone meant not having to argue over the music choice and no one pushing for the pop country station which drilled a hole in my skull with the same fifteen songs of artificial guitar twang. I wondered how the rest of the crew fared with the packages and if they would squeeze enough bees out of that third yard if they had to move a fourth. We needed a little over a hundred packa….SHIT!

A grandma hit the brakes in front of me at the first flash of green turning to yellow, and I was forced to slam mine, jolting the steering wheel, the cab, and everything on the back. The truck's grill stopped a few feet from the grandma's bumper, but before I could take a breath I heard a sickening thud to my rear-left. In the mirror I saw the smashed remains of a hive lying on the pavement with bees roiling on the timber. The next moment I was greeted with the red and blue flashing lights from the police car I hadn't noticed in the lane behind me.

"Oh, no," I whispered. The situation had just gone from ugly to code red. I flew out of the truck, but a quick sting on my cheek sent me back to the passenger seat for my veil which had its strings caught in something, perhaps the door. I yanked it until the strings broke, threw the veil on my head, and ran back to the broken hive. The policeman had opened his door and stood out of his seat, but when he saw my veil, he quickly sat back down and closed the cruiser's door. Bees crawled on the ground and filled the air with angry buzzing and a sting every few seconds as I shoved the combs back in the box and tossed it into the empty space on the pallet. In the adjoining lane, a small girl in the backseat of a car watched this scene with true horror, something I am certain haunted her nightmares for weeks to come. The traffic light turned green, and cars began to move. The police car pulled alongside of me. I leaned over with the best old-fashioned Texas grin I could muster, waiting for him to open the window, but when I jerked in pain from another sting on the arm, he shook his head and drove through the intersection, killing his flashing lights and moving away from me.

Really? I thought, cleaning up the final bits of debris, getting stung a few more times. Really? I climbed in the cab and took off my veil. The light turned yellow again, then red. The bees tumbled around the left side of the truck, confused and furious. Other drivers looked at the strange horror from inside the safety of their cars. When the light turned green I pressed the gas pedal, wondering if the cop was waiting for me somewhere ahead. But there was no sign of him. I tried to breathe normally and began picking the stingers out my face, neck, and arms. The afterglow of venom began to heat up different parts of my body.

Only when I found the turn for Oil Pad and swung the gate closed was I able to take a full breath. I vowed to check for ropes in every truck I got and to pester Binford once again to let me take a morning off so I could get my official CDL. I drove gingerly down the gravel road, turned a corner, and came upon a pump jack working away, slowly pulling oil from the earth.

"Another day in bee paradise," I thought and began to suit up for the day's final battle.

6

Driving North

2005

Great Christ, I was driving north. My car, which had been pointed this way for the past five hours, gunned for the cool weather like a horse heading back to the barn. Once the May page had been flipped on local calendars and the heat and humidity began their torturous slow-motion tango, Texas was not a fun place to be. Maybe the summer was bearable for the desk jockeys and those who enjoyed a close relationship with their air conditioner, or if you happened to be a jalapeño on the vine, then life under the furnace-gray sky was good. But when laboring outside in a full-body suit like a Hazmat worker investigating a virus outbreak in a sauna, life felt cruel indeed.

For the past two Texas summer months I had entertained this daydream: driving through a Rocky Mountain pass with crusty snowbanks still clinging to the side of the road, pulling over, stepping out of the car, and letting the cool wind brush my skin until I was shivering blue. Knowing that this would soon come true, my right foot weighed heavily on the gas pedal, and I had to check myself every now and then so I wouldn't give Texas' finest any excuse to hold me back.

Hill country was long gone. I had just skirted between the twin steel devils Dallas and Fort Worth without incident, and the panhandle was my next destination. Every second I left behind a hundred feet of sunbaked tarmac. Steady hours of feeling the pulse of the road, the evolving passage of a long drive through the Southwest, the landscape changing with the arc of the sun; these are sensations I wish everyone could experience. Seeing the scene in miniature from a plane window is not the same: one needs to be at ground-level with the plains, watching the Rockies grow in the distance under the blood-blue sky, knowing that it won't be long before the car will be hugging the center line on tight, twisting roads in a different country altogether.

In addition to that list, I must include ample time for the trip, a ripe curiosity, and good companions. Driving across an unknown state where no back road is too outlandish or side trip too bothersome are the proper conditions for such a journey. Too, the thrill of not knowing where you are going to sleep that coming night and being open to any unexpected experience that may come might complete the picture of the ultimate road trip.

In the years prior to this, I had driven up and across the US several times both with and without friends, checking off all of the boxes above. This time I did not have much space for leisure, but I did have some unusual ride-alongs: ten small colonies of honey bees, each in a container the size of a shoebox—thin wood on the short sides, bottoms, and tops, and mesh on the long sides. The bees—three pounds in each box—clustered around their queen who was trapped in a small cage alongside a metal can which slowly dripped sugar syrup to feed them.

We had shaken these packages from Texan yards the day before, and they were heading to beekeepers in Colorado. While it is possible to send bees that far by overnight mail, the bees had a much better chance of good health and survival if they spent less time in the hands of the postal service. The plan was for me to drop off these packages at a post office in Denver, and the next day they would be delivered to various parts of the state to start their productive lives. The best part of this exchange was watching the postman's face when he saw the address label attached to the piece of wood between him and a few thousand stinging insects. But it's legal—you can send live animals through USPS. Order baby chicks online and in a few days you will find a chorus of peeping in a box on your doorstep.

During package season, this was Barry's full-time job. He loaded a van in Texas and drove around the country at an unfathomable pace: three-day loops where he would drop packages off in post offices from Washington state to Minnesota, blast back to Texas to reload, and then burn up to Pennsylvania. We would be toiling in the field, shaking packages in the 90° F heat and whip-cream thick humid air, but when Barry appeared after a few eighteen hour days on the road, he'd look more beat than we did. It was a good lesson about the hardships of long-distance driving that snuffed out any remaining dreams I had of being a trucker. I took this small load of packages because it was on my way north; I would spend the rest of the summer pulling honey in Montana. The bees would keep me company for half the ride.

Honey bees have a distinct smell. Inside the hive their scent is masked by the surrounding wax and honey, but when they are separated from this, pounds of bees by themselves, their smell stands out: sweet, earthy, moist, and almost meaty. Though they weren't typical road trip companions—I didn't get many stories or jokes to help pass the time—they were a good fit for this trip. I played easy music, cracked the car's windows for fresh air, and pulled over every now and then to mist them with water.

After passing Dallas I pointed towards Wichita Falls, the hometown of one of my high school friends. Though he currently wasn't there, I thought I would at least see his old stomping grounds. I called him on the way into town, the first time we had talked in years, and he gave me two recommendations for a quick burger.

After finding a shaded parking spot at the first of these, I opened the back of my car and inspected the packages. The bees clung to each other and buzzed as I shifted their crates. I dug the spray bottle out of the backseat's clutter which, after only a half-day on the road, was already threatening to spread throughout car.

I gave each package a strong misting, hoping that this, cracked windows, and shade would keep them going while I ate inside. A curious father of a passing-by family glanced at what I was doing. He asked, "What the heck are those?"

"Honey bees," I said as the rest of the family gathered around the car. The kids pressed their hands against the glass, but their courage failed when I offered to take one of the packages out for a closer look. Dad reached back into his memory and told me about a TV report he once heard about how important bees were, as if I, a beekeeper, didn't know this already, but I nodded along and added details for the kids.

"It's darn interesting," he said. "I've never met a beekeeper before." It wasn't the first time I heard this sentiment, and I might have said the same thing five years earlier when beekeeping wasn't yet on my horizon. "People do the strangest things," he said as we parted ways.

I entered the restaurant—a family-run BBQ joint that looked like it developed its signature flavor from a well-worn and infrequently cleaned grill—and found an empty table underneath a wall covered in license plates, framed newspaper articles and mounted animal skulls. I ordered and then opened the book I was reading—*The Crossing* by Cormac McCarthy, a brutal southwestern saga that reminded me that my current trip was rather cushy compared to those days. I only read a few words before I gave up and listened to the Wichitan gossip coming from the table behind me. The group further up the table, sensing a foreigner in their midst, asked me where I was from. The conversation unfolded not unlike my last one with the father and ended on the same note: people do the strangest things. My new-found acquaintances left as my burger arrived, and I could see them almost shaking their heads at that thought.

The burger was decent, as road burgers went, and I was glad to have found some place to eat that wasn't a seedy pit stop a hundred feet off the highway. With my soiled napkin on the plate, I stood up to pay, but the waiter told me the bill was taken care of. I looked around. No one lifted their glass towards me; everyone continued with their burger and conversation.

Perplexed, I left the restaurant, started the car, and drove back to the highway. Who paid for my meal? Was it the father from the parking lot? The chatty people at my table? Did my friend who recommended the place pay for my meal? If it was him, how did he know which of his two recommendations I would choose? And how did he pay the bill? The mystery, which is still unsolved, churned in my head as I pushed further north, where the sun morphed from a white heat to deepening oranges and yellows across the flatlands.

As it grew dark I left the highway for a smaller route that would take me through the Oklahoma panhandle. It wasn't the fastest course to Denver, but the geographical strangeness of that thin stretch of state was something I wanted to see. I started scoping out the variety of mid-land hotels scooting by: small hotels. Gas station hotels. Trucker hotels. Paper-thin-wall hotels next to florescent XXX strip club signs. Part of the funding for this trip included a night at a hotel, but the sorry examples along this road didn't inspire a closer examination. I stopped for a gas-station coffee that tasted like genuine local cow dirt, but with four sugars and two creams it became passable.

Back on the road I realized that on the ground, and in the dark, the panhandle looked fairly similar to the rest of North Texas: plains, stretching far and wide. Feeling a pang of loneliness, I called my high-school friend Ryan. We chatted for a while as my car zipped through the night, our conversation and the coffee keeping me awake.

The night was deep when I shot out of Oklahoma's barrel into New Mexico, a state which I had only previously been in for a matter of hours, but one I felt an unexplained affinity for. I drove towards Raton and remembered a song called, "Snowing on Raton." The radio had been a good companion thus far on the journey, but I could feel the darkness and the full day of driving begin to weigh down on me. Just outside of town, I turned onto a side road, drove a quarter of a mile, and parked in the driveway of a gated field. When I switched off the car, the silence of the landscape flooded in along with exquisitely cool air. In the back of the car, which was already a mess, I rearranged my stuff, shifting a backpack, cooler, and loose clothes onto the passenger seat to create a small alley in the center, just enough for my body to fit. When I climbed into this nest, I was neatly tucked between my stuff on one side and the packages of bees on the other, with my feet threaded between the two front seats. It was not exactly comfortable, but it would work for a few hours.

The bees buzzed softly and shifted in the packages. Tomorrow, I would be in Denver by noon, and the bees and I would part ways. They would continue their journey to a new home while I kept moving north towards the cool Rocky Mountains to meet their cousins working the vast alfalfa fields of Montana.

7

Montana Recital

2008

The honey pump, our steady yet unseen friend, had suddenly turned into the source of all our problems. Its one and only job was to propel honey from a small settling tank in the extracting room into a giant holding tank twenty feet away. During the previous week the settling tank began to overflow at increasingly reduced intervals, and we would stop for ten minutes, twenty, or more while waiting for the pump to catch up. After a few days it stopped pumping at all, like a gear spinning without teeth. None of our inexpert prodding could get it back into any semblance of normal functioning, but Craig was on it.

A goofy fellow in his mid-thirties, Craig was our manager. He looked stunningly like a version of Tom Petty who had spent his adult life working on a farm instead of being a rock star. When we realized the pump was going to die, Craig put out an order, and a new pump began to creep towards us across the open plains. When he called the postal service this morning, they said it would probably arrive the following day, but they had said that the day before, and maybe even the day before that. With the uncapper and extractor sitting dormant, the hot room soon had honey supers piled to the ceiling. We organized the warehouse and cleaned the equipment, but with the real boss in another zip code, and with Craig being a seriously laid-back dude, there wasn't much motivation to do these chores at more than a basic level.

After lunch, Craig left to pull honey from one last yard while Paula, Dave, and I spent the rest of the day taking extended coffee breaks, examining every grimy corner of the break room and searching for topics to complain about. Paula waited until 4 PM before she cracked open a bottle of strawberry vodka and mixed it with lemonade. It was a killer combination for a bored-as-butternuts summer afternoon.

Jake, Paula's thirteen-year old son, poured the drinks. The week before, he and Paula brought me to a field by their house where I shot a .45 handgun for the first time which, without ear protection, probably destroyed part of my hearing. Then Jake lit a small bomb he had crafted out of ten packages of sparklers duct-taped together and blew an old 55-gallon honey drum surprisingly far off the ground. The explosion made us hoot and holler and laugh, and then we went back to the house for another round of drinks, thankfully with all fingers and appendages still intact.

When the Freightliner bumped onto the gravel behind the shop, we pushed back our chairs and piled onto the loading dock to see Craig climbing down from the cab. Already feeling warm from our first round, we analyzed and derided Craig's forklift abilities as he transferred the pallets of honey supers onto the dock, but he completed the task without incident, and we then stuffed the pallets into the final free spots of the hot room.

With the day's work now truly finished, Dave went home while Paula, Craig, and I retired to the break room for another drink. Paula, a Montana farm girl with strawberry blonde hair, was the conversational motor in this outfit. "Those poor city kids…" Paula said, referring to Jake's friend Toby who had accidentally run over his grandfather's leg with a lawnmower a few weeks earlier. "They don't know jack-@%#&-shit." Then she glanced at Jake and said to me, "Don't swear in front of your kids, when you got 'em… if you got 'em. My father would never use the F word in front of me. He'd say everything else in the book, but not that." She then proceeded to use that word ten more times in the next few minutes. "Some good mother I am," she snorted.

I was already fully aware of this odd situation; the bright-pink motel where I had been living for the past month was owned by Toby's family, and grandpa was still hobbling around on crutches. What I didn't fully grasp was how she considered Toby a "city kid" because he lived in a town of 6,000, and Jake, whose house was in the fields only three miles away, was not. These are important distinctions to a Montanan, I suppose.

Jake, who at thirteen was not only the bartender but also his mother's designated driver, was beginning to see the end of the rainbow and pushed his mother towards the door. "Whatever blows up your skirt," Paula told him and said goodbye to us. The day was over, and I could go home as well, but my evening entertainment at the pink motel would probably be eating a sandwich while watching the train yard across the street, followed by the audio version of *Beverley Hills Chihuahua* that transmitted to my room's clock radio from a drive-in movie theater a mile away. But, no. I had already taken a few steps down the path and agreed to continue when Craig said, "Let's go see what Troy's up to."

Still in our sweaty work clothes, a Megadeth CD playing loudly in his truck, we drove to the dive-bar in Billings where Craig's roommate Troy worked. As I got out of the truck, a sheaf of papers clustered around my foot-well and tumbled onto the pavement. "No worries," Craig told me, "those are just bills."

We ordered a pitcher of beer, and shots of Jose Cuervo magically arrived alongside it. We raised our shots to Troy, threw them back, and then returned to our conversation about the honey spinner. Craig described in great detail how it took him many years to learn its finicky nature. It was a custom-made sideways spinner; the frames first went through an automatic uncapper then pushed along two conveyor belts that loaded them into the drum twenty at a time. In theory, stuffing the spinner should have been as efficient as stuffing a turkey, but in practice the frames were always askew, stuck, and crashing to the floor. It was his father's machine, Craig told me with a complex mix of pride and sadness. The honey operation was once owned by his father, but it had been bought by a larger, migratory beekeeping operation, and Craig still worked there as "the manager". I didn't know the full story, but I had seen this sentiment in him a few times—a flash of disappointment, like modern times were a little too fast.

When the beer pitcher was reduced to foam, another one appeared with its Cuervo courtiers. We were on the far side of the curve now; the stress of the work-day drowned and tunneled toward something deeper. The slope was slippery. Troy took a break from bartending to join us for a drink and a laugh. After a pizza and another pitcher, we left the bar. My hand couldn't even find my wallet before Craig threw money on the table, covering everything, and I knew he only had five dollars left until the next pay check. Both he and Paula were beacons of generosity, and I told myself for the umpteenth time that I would one day be like them.

We climbed in Craig's truck, papers once again falling out the foot-well. I stuffed most of them back in. Craig drove back to my motel, but not to drop me off. Though it was by all means bedtime, earlier in the bar we had planned a fourth leg of the evening, one that seemed so strange that I couldn't refuse. I ran inside, grabbed a bulky, hard suitcase, and put it in the back of the truck.

We drove up the mesa north of the city blasting Metallica's "Ride the Lightning". On the ride, Craig told me a story about how he was once invited to a Hutterite community for what he called "Mating Day". The Hutterites are groups of people living in farming communities on the Montana grasslands—from a simple outsider's perspective, they seemed like the Amish if the Amish had adopted modern technology but kept the style. We had a few bee yards on their properties and had once stopped by their compound—I saw dorms and aquaculture tanks—to drop off honey. They were a fairly closed society, Craig told me, and sometimes needed new blood. Certain locals of "good German stock" as Craig was would be invited where a woman would lay on the bed under a sheet with a hole in it, and the visitor would perform his business. This act occurred under the gaze of the woman's husband, who would be sitting in the corner with his arms folded across his chest, making sure no true passion unfolded.

Craig said he didn't go. I didn't know if such things were true—it sounds like a local legend that high-schoolers probably snigger over—but at that moment my fuzzy mind thought it sounded sensible.

Tipping over the rim of the mesa, the Billings airport appeared before us. The wide landscape and golden glow of security floodlights on the industrial buildings surrounded by barbed wire gave the impression of a top-secret research complex. Craig drove to the gate, and he told the guard we were here to see Dean. That password unlocked the airport security system, and the gate's arm lifted. Craig drove down the access corridor and then straight into the hanger where a handful of small aircraft sat dormant, and where Dean stood in the open door of a plane. Dean, Craig's good buddy, cleaned private jets at the Billings Airport. He ducked back in the plane and came out with three beers.

"Dean, you gotta hear this guy play the accordion." That was my introduction. Craig had heard me play the squeezebox one Sunday afternoon when I was tired of the pink motel and had come to the honey house in the fields where I could play as loudly as I liked. Craig had dropped by to pick something up and was pretty floored that I not only had the instrument, but that I could play it.

Dean dragged over a couple of chairs and a milk crate for himself. As I unpacked my accordion and put it on my chest, I felt a gust of clear thought that said: what? The moment opened up before me; of all the places I had been and would be in the future, this was a truly weird one: an accordion recital for an airport worker in Billings, Montana at 11 PM on a Thursday evening. But there I was, playing the best, stupid exercise-book ditties I knew: "Beautiful Dreamer", "Bicycle Built for Two", "Red River Valley". Yet, as Craig assured me he would, Dean really did seem to like them. It wasn't a farce; I was playing for someone who really enjoyed the accordion. I played every song I knew by heart, flubbing them half the time but pushing through with what I could. I played until we finished our beers.

As a wind down, Dean gave us a tour of the airport—the inside of a few private jets, the cold war nuclear facility, his locker room, a stack of porno magazines in a locker: the usual airport things. But then someone on the radio told Dean to get back to work, and Craig and I said a quick goodbye.

On the drive down the mesa, the clustered lights of Billings city beneath us, Craig turned down the metal music.

"Gosh," he said, "I hope the pump comes tomorrow, or we will have another day like today."

8

North Dakota Sun

2008

❧

The North Dakota sun has a quality of its own. When unimpeded by clouds, the sun glazes across the massive canvas of a sky, turning these high northern plains into a radically different place. Summer mornings are long, the evenings longer, and in between the full, flaring globe radiates down without that nasty southern bite. Instead, it licks or nuzzles in a gentle reminder that this kindness won't last very long.

I awoke from quickly forgotten dreams. Intense, but fleeting. This was a symptom of traveling; the first few nights or weeks after landing in a new place, my dreams increased in vibrancy and strangeness as if my spirit needed some time to bang about the room before settling down. Now, after adapting to the space, I no longer needed the first ten seconds of consciousness to place where I was in the world. The sun lit up the translucent curtain of my room like an incandescent bulb.

I was in Moffit, North Dakota. Moffit had about two-hundred people living in it, and the sole business was a bar. Other than the two summers I spent working deep in Bob Marshall wilderness and Glacier National Park, this was as remote as I had ever lived. My home town in Western Massachusetts was smallish with a population of 1,500, but in the crowded northeast each town was a cell surrounded by others in the state organism. It only took a few minutes' drive over an arbitrary border before you could cash a check, buy a roll of toilet paper, or take out a book from the library. Towns on the western plain had a distinctly different feel to them. They were islands of civilization in an ocean of farmland. A gas station with a tiny store required a twenty-minute drive from Moffit, while real groceries, entertainment, or any medical treatment meant an hour-long trip into Bismarck. Even in that outpost, the options of the above were not what I would call exceptional.

Lying in bed, I watched the dust motes floating in the air and floral wallpaper peeling in the upper corner. The first steps of the day, I realized, would be recovery from a small hangover. The previous night, like many nights here, was spent in a bar, or multiple bars; we hopped across the county as if Bud Light might taste better in a seat twenty minutes away. And in these places it was difficult to relax and nurse a beer. They kept flowing from the fridge like an assembly line. When someone came by for a chat, an extra bottle would arrive with them. Say something comical, and a signal to the bartender would crack another cold one. Whoever won a big pot from the pull tabs bought everyone a round. New faces entered the bar, and new Bud Lights were doled out. I tried to parse out this phenomenon one inebriated evening: was it generosity and kindness? Or was it a coerced steering towards group drunkenness? Probably some of both. Either way, at the end of most nights, I found a small family of beers on the counter next to me, as I fought the losing battle to take down each sibling.

I was guided into this local scene by Barry—my manager, my housemate, my drinking partner. I had first worked with Barry in Texas, a state he criticized to no end and frequently pined to escape. "You know what the best part of Texas is?" he often asked me. "The sign that says: Welcome to Oklahoma." A thousand miles north, I found a different side of Barry. He had a deep love for North Dakota. Some years prior, after a broken affair where his ex-wife took the house, business, and basically everything that wasn't in his pickup, Barry drove here from Pennsylvania and decided it was the place for him. Plenty of open space, kooky old farmers, and cold Bud Light—what more did he need?

Barry was in his early sixties, gray-bearded, bespectacled, and constantly wore jeans, a jean shirt, suspenders, and a dark blue ball cap. His breast pocket was the snug home to a pack of Turkish Silver cigarettes, which he would demolish throughout the day. Driving his personal truck, he'd light a cigarette with a match and toss the burnt stick down in the footwell, where there was, honestly, around two to three inches of blackened matches. There would be more, he told me, but he had recently cleaned it out after the time he was driving 70 mph on the highway and a smoldering match started a small fire about his feet.

Barry and I got along well. If you worked hard, followed instructions, and didn't kick down his bedroom door at 3 AM demanding a better salary like that pair of South African beekeepers he once told me about, you could be on his good list. Even then, Barry gave those beekeepers a few minutes to pack their veils before a pre-dawn ride to the Bismarck airport. Barry was a nice guy.

Hangover or not, the day would probably progress like any other day here. Barry and I would have our breakfast, get in the truck and drive three minutes across town to the workshop to meet the extracting team. This was a handful of locals, one of them being Lee, a sprightly eighty-year-old fellow whose grandfather had founded Moffit. Lee couldn't sit still for a minute, and whatever he did when he wasn't sitting still usually meant trouble. It seemed he could undo an hour's work in a few unattended moments. Smoke breaks were the most dangerous time; instead of shooting the shit with everyone outside, he would sneak back in the shop and start doing something which in his mind was helpful, but in everyone else's was decidedly the opposite. Barry eventually found a solution as eternal as it was entertaining. He gave Lee a swatter and told him to take care of the flies in the shop. In a North Dakotan summer, flies are about as common as sunflowers. Lee took the job very seriously.

After putting the extracting team to work, Barry and I would get in the Freightliner and drive into the plains. There were perhaps forty bee locations, forty to sixty hives in each, within an hour's radius around the shop. Each morning we would drive in one direction—twenty, thirty, forty minutes—and pull honey from a few yards. These agricultural grasslands, from South Dakota to Alberta, are a honey-making paradise. Fields of clover, alfalfa and sunflowers stretched to the horizon, and on good summer days when the flowers bristled with nectar, a strong hive can gather over ten pounds of honey. The hives were stacked tall—four or five supers, sometimes taller than I was—with the most pure and delicious white clover honey. This is opposed to other parts of the country—Florida, for example—where nectar drips once or twice per year, and they are lucky to fill a single super with a dark, over-flavored honey that wins no awards.

After driving for miles through open, rolling plains, Barry would turn onto an obscure dirt road which didn't look any different from the last six dirt roads we passed, come around a bend, and coast straight into a small city of hives.

Pulling honey—taking off full boxes of honey from hives and putting them on the truck—is not the most fun job. It takes a strong back and a weak mind, so the saying goes. The main hassle is removing bees from the comb. It's easier if you use an extra piece of equipment called a "bee escape", but this requires multiple trips to the yard. You can also brush the bees from each comb, but that takes too much time at a large scale. Usually, we used a chemical called Butyric anhydride, fondly known as "Bee Go". It smells horrible, like if you used Red Bull as a nasal spray, and if a drop gets on your clothes or, heaven help you, your skin, you will have clear nostrils for the next twelve hours no matter how hard you try to scrub it off. This "Bee Go" is dribbled onto a piece of cloth which is then put on the top of the hive. The bees hate the scent, and on a sunny day the chemical expands with warmth so that the bees move downward, out of the supers, to get as far away from it as possible.

It was hard, honest work. We heaved heavy boxes off the hives and onto the truck. I felt blood coursing through me, prickles of sweat on my skin, muscles tiring and strengthening. Barry let go a groan like he would expire every time he picked up a box, or put down a box, or climbed into the truck, or sat down in his easy chair at the end of the day—knee and hip pains from a life of hard work, self-medicated with Bud Light. Yet, he not only kept up with me, forty years his junior, but he out-worked me most of the time. When the weather was fine, under a dense blue sky, we would work without talking, watching our labor pile up on the truck, feeling the industry of the bees in every box: the physicality of completing something which would put food on the table.

Barry and I would pull honey from three or four yards before the truck was full. Sometimes a lunch at a small-town pit stop was in order. Otherwise, we would be back at the shop around quitting time to unload, check the progress of honey extraction, lock up, and then start the post-work parade once again. Another cold one down the hatch.

Bud Lights, though only a few shades of alcohol stronger than dirty water, still added up in the system over the course of a strong evening. My mind clicked awake at the realization that it was already past 8 AM, our normal starting time, but Barry hadn't banged on my door. Maybe he was also hungover and still in bed. Either way, a tall glass of water called my name.

In the living room I found Barry in the thick of his morning routine: sitting in the corner chair with a laptop on a wooden board in front of him, head tilted slightly back so he could see the game of solitaire through his bifocals, TV on in the background. As I walked in he cracked open a can of hyper-sweet iced tea. Two empty cans of the same stood on the nearby side table.

"Morning," I groaned.

"Morning," he grunted back, and I continued into the kitchen where I gulped down a glass or water and began to feel life flowing through me. Minutes passed and coffee prepared itself without a coherent thought forming in my head. A fly buzzed against the window while a few of its cousins lay dead on the sill below. One memory from the previous evening splashed back when I opened the fridge for milk and saw a full shelf of Bud Light bottles: each of us hugging a six-pack as we left the bar, then a twenty-minute dirt road drive among spooked pheasants and a bounding family of deer. With a steaming mug of coffee, I shuffled back to the living room. Barry's position hadn't changed. He clicked a few more times.

"Big doings in The Big Apple, today."

I looked at the TV. The national news, September 16, 2008. Lehman Brothers at 0.00. Numbers crawling across the screen. Banks scrambling. Stocks plummeting. Shocked faces. Everything red, down, negative. I took a sip of coffee and tried to turn on my brain.

"I told everyone to take the morning off. Would be kind fun to see this circus fall apart."

If the stock market crashed that morning, I wondered, what would happen in North Dakota? Looking at Barry, who focused on his game as if the TV hosts were gushing over a new diet fad instead of the collapse of our economic system, perhaps not so much. Barry clicked a few more times and smirked.

"Got one." The computer sounded a chime at his solitaire success. I sat on the couch and rubbed my eyes.

New York City seemed far, far away.

9

Texas Test

2008

I arrived at the DMV office at 10:30 AM on an early December morning. Getting out of the truck I marveled at the white dust brushed over every surface: it was the first snow this part of Texas had seen in around twenty years. What was the luck that my commercial driver's license test was on a day with inexperienced winter drivers and slick roads? And that it was my final chance to pass as I was leaving Texas the following day? I felt the brewing of a perfect storm when at the entrance I bumped into a kid, beet-red in the face, hurling obscenities behind him. His target of rage was the squat, three-hundred-pound lady with rubbery cheeks sitting behind the high wooden desk: the matron of the DMV.

The kid must have been a novice to the DMV procedure. I already had enough experience to know that she was absolutely in charge of this domain. There was no point in arguing or getting angry; once you stepped through that door she was the captain, governor, and sheriff, and you had to submit yourself to her and hope for a kind bequest.

Thankfully, Mrs. DMV appeared unperturbed from the confrontation. She blandly inspected a piece of paper in her hand as I removed my hat and approached the desk.

"Hello, ma'am. Remember me?" Mrs. DMV's eyes rolled upwards to meet mine. I continued, "I'm here for my road test."

She glanced at the paper again and began to rise from her chair. "Well …" Her words curled in a perfect Texas drawl. "Let's do it."

I put on my hat and headed for the door.

"I hope your truck's got heat, sonny," she said. "I forgot my jacket at home." She was wearing a thin, pink pullover.

"Umm, well, no," I replied. "The heater's broken, sorry. But you can … borrow one of mine?" I had on four layers of clothing and began taking off my heavy hooded sweatshirt.

She sighed. "Oh, crap. Let's just go."

Outside, the cold once again shocked me. After a summer of nearly baking in my own juices, the coldness appeared like an unwelcome stranger. My breath came out in white puffs. Thin snowflakes drifted down. Mrs. DMV was not pleased with the anomalous conditions.

"Start it up and show me your lights."

I climbed into the cab and turned the key. She stood in front of the truck and pointed her clipboard to the left. I hit the blinker. She pointed to the right and I switched. She made a slashing motion across her throat. I cut the engine and opened the door.

"Right blinker doesn't work. You can't take the test."

"What?"

The poor two-ton Freightliner had led a rough life. The odometer was stuck at 190,000 miles, which was by our best estimate over 100,000 dirt-road-miles ago. The speedometer was unresponsive, as was the fuel gauge. It had no heat, no AC, and a passenger window that was stuck half way down. It was a rolling piece of scrap metal that we would keep driving until the axles gave out, it caught fire, or when I got it stuck in a mud pit deep enough that it wasn't worth the tow fee. Plus, we had just fixed that right blinker the other day.

"Did you hear me?" Her voice gained an additional heft.

"Yes. I ... I mean ..."

"Sorry, sonny," she said. "Get it fixed and come back." She was already on the way back to the warmth inside. I kicked the tire and hopped in the cab. Do they care that I'm illegally driving the vehicle to and from the license test? I whipped the truck out of the parking lot, Bobcat trailer skidding behind me, and pointed to the auto shop across town. For the next forty-five minutes the mechanic and I poked and prodded at the blinker's connection under the hood, discovering that it functioned perfectly with a little downward pressure. The mechanic positioned it just right and closed the casing. "Don't hit any bumps," he told me as I climbed back into the cab.

I arrived back at the DMV feeling fuzzy, frazzled, and nervous. The snow had stopped, though the dusting remained. When I coaxed Mrs. DMV back out into the cold, the blinker behaved itself. After a heart-pounding straight-line reverse test with the long bed and short Bobcat trailer wobbling back and forth behind me, Mrs. DMV opened the door and grunted her way into the cab. The passenger seat-belt, which we had reinstalled specifically for this road test, stretched to its full length across Mrs. DMV's body. I whispered a small prayer and eased the truck out of the parking lot and onto the main road.

The driving test started well, other than Mrs. DMV's pained look when she realized that the passenger side window was broken and wouldn't fully roll up. I focused on the road: using my turn signal, staying between the lines, and even stopping for an old lady at a crosswalk. At the first stoplight, I turned right, and after straightening the wheel, Mrs. DMV made a mark on her clipboard.

"You touch that gearshift when you're turning again and I fail you."

"Yes, ma'am," I said with a burst of heat spreading through me. I didn't remember reading this anywhere in the manual nor could I understand why this was a rule, but I realized I had to play by it.

We rode in silence for a few minutes. Snow started again, and I hit the windshield wiper. The driver's side wiper lay dead on the hood while the passenger's side waved like a madman. I glanced over and saw the clipboard laying face-down on her lap, her attention drifting outside the cab. We came to a long bend in the road, and, as I straightened out, a bright neon sign appeared in the distance. Lunch time was approaching. An idea popped into my head.

"Boy," I sighed, "I sure am hungry." My voice sounded wooden and fake like the beginning of a bad infomercial, but the hook was cast.

"Oh, god, I know," she moaned, her voice shifting from DMV Matron into a that of a human's. I thought for a moment, and then jigged on the lure.

"I just arrived in town, do you know where to get a good hamburger?"

She bit. "Well, there's Carrol's over on Main. Then there's The Burger Barn right here ..." The neon sign and red building flashed by. "They make a mean Mushroom & Swiss," she said, pulling her pink sweater a little tighter around her.

"What about a bacon cheeseburger?" I asked, jamming the clutch and shifting into fourth gear. That question set her on a monologue about the pros and cons of every restaurant in town: the burgers at Western Club were only good with bacon. The Circle H had only decent burgers, but the people who worked there were nice. Grandma's Kitchen made a juicy, thick burger, and I had to try their milkshake too. Even McDonald's across town was okay because, "Sometimes," she said, "you just need it."

I nodded along, but little pass/fail details kept popping in my head. Was I driving the speed limit? Did I fully stop behind that line? Am I looking around enough? She continued talking. A minute after a stop sign, I realized that I had unconsciously shifted in the middle of the turn. Had she noticed? Would I fail? Little bullets of sweat popped out on my brow. She hadn't said anything, but I wondered if it was all over.

Soon, I slowed at a red light. When it changed to green, I hit the gas and turned the steering wheel. In the middle of her description of the condiments at Grandma's Kitchen, Mrs. DMV abruptly cut the sentence short. All her attention beamed on my right hand which hovered, frozen, two inches above the gear shift. The engine roared and the RPM needle dove deep into the orange-red zone. We both sat like statues as the truck hurtled through the intersection.

As soon as I hit the straight-a-way, I pressed the clutch, slammed the shifter into second gear, and the truck roared with relief. She made a mark on her clipboard before continuing her sentence. Grandma's Kitchen made some good condiments, apparently.

When I pulled into the DMV's lot the lady seemed surprised to be back. I parked the truck, turned off the engine, and confronted the fatal moment. She looked at her clipboard and scribbled for ten lifelong seconds. Then she said, "Yeah, you're good," hopped out of the cab, and dashed back into the heated office. The warm-glow of relief filled the truck.

With the proper paperwork in my pocket, I roared out of the DMV's driveway, shifting into 2nd as I twisted the steering wheel. Only a few hours stood between me and two months of vacation. The next day I would start my road trip to New Orleans, Alabama, Georgia, and then north to Massachusetts. The way back to the shop took me on the same route of my test, and when the neon sign appeared, I hit the blinker, which by now had probably failed. There was a mean Mushroom & Swiss with my name on it.

10

Texas Moment

2009

It was a long day, but it was a good day. The tiredness wasn't overwhelming; the bees were distracted by a honey flow, and we had just reached the best seasonal weather Texas had to offer. With the winter chill gone, bluebonnets flooded the roadsides, and we still had some weeks before the furnace cranked to 11—Texas has a downright enjoyable New England summer tucked somewhere between March and May. It was the kind of day where I could trip over a pallet hidden in the tall grass and tumble to the ground with a laugh instead of a facefull of cow pie.

Danny drove the pickup while I rode in the passenger seat with my arm out the window. I don't know what childhood experience instilled this in me, but an open car window on a warm afternoon is a hard feeling to top. Danny and I had been shaking packages with the crew all day, but the last yard had come up a few short for the order that would ship out the following morning. As the other guys went back to the shop, Danny and I loaded two shaker boxes, the scale, and the remaining five packages into his truck and pushed on to the next yard for the day's coda.

If Keith in New Zealand had been my elementary beekeeping teacher, Danny brought me through high school and into college. My first dash of Texan reality was the sound of his drawl over the phone as we talked the winter before I would graduate. He hired me sight unseen, hazarding a chance that this fresh-from-college Northerner would be able to handle a commercial beekeeping workload based on the interest in honey bees alone. When I arrived, I found truth to some predictable details about Danny—he was the 4th generation of an apicultural family and knew his honey bees in and out—and others that were surprising—he had a Ph.D. in molecular biology and, on top of this, a degree in law. My expectations of "Texan beekeeper" were shattered.

Many beekeepers, when their businesses grow into thousands of colonies, move into the office while crews of hired laborers head out into the bee fields. "Desk beekeepers", we call them. But that wasn't Danny's priority. Most days he was sweating in the bee yard with the crew, keeping an eye on the quality and state of his colonies while we shook

packages together. Because of this, he taught me to read a hive and laid the foundation of my beekeeping career. Later on, I met commercial beeks who run their operation like a factory line—the manager makes the decision on what needs to happen to a yard while the workers do the same thing to every hive. Only then did I become very thankful that Danny encouraged an individual approach. He taught us to evaluate each colony independently and work together as a crew to make the entire yard better.

Another thing I didn't truly appreciate at the time was Danny's commitment to breeding against varroa. When varroa first arrived in the US in 1987, many beekeepers turned to chemicals while Danny and Binford chose to select queens for mite resistance. I heard the early years were difficult for them, but good genetics and breeding methodology allowed them to push past the hump so that their bees developed resistance. With New Zealand being my first beekeeping experience (where there was no varroa at the time) and Texas being my second (where they had already done the hard work against it), my first years in the beekeeping field were spent blissfully naive of varroa difficulties. It wasn't until I moved to other operations and began the chemical warfare against varroa did I realize how special that was.

Danny pulled off the main road and crunched onto gravel. We drove a few minutes to a locked gate, and I stood outside. Gate swinging is part of the procedure in Texas, like putting on your boots. I was familiar with all varieties—the easy swing, the metal hasp, the simple latch, the electric hook, the padlock code, the put-your-full-weight-behind-it tension gap—as well as the tricks to oil them through. This one had a daisy chain of locks so that fourteen different people could get into the paddock without having to share a key. I fitted the key in our lock, clicked it open, and pushed the gate forward.

A few cows ambled towards us, hoping we were bringing them dinner. Mounds of grass soaked up the late afternoon light. I leaned against the gate, the truck passing through, its chrome body gaining an additional dimension. The sound of the engine firing, the gravel under tire, the heat of the late afternoon air, the mass of tree branches above me ending each in a delicate leaf, the rough bark sending water up and taking solar energy down. Details around me obtained a sudden sharpness. Seconds gained weight, and each passed trembling. I didn't know why this moment was important, merely opening a gate and letting the truck pass through, but it was. I felt something inside me, simple and emergent, cutting deeper into the unknown. I am here. This is Steinbeck's time. We live and breathe and work.

Maybe I was just dehydrated.

I closed the gate. It is a tenant of life: to leave a gate as you found it. Back in the truck, Danny drove us past the disappointed cows, downhill along a two-track dirt road and around a curve until we saw a collection of hives still active in the waning day.

The moment passed, but its impression lingered. I thought of the distance from Massachusetts to Texas. My drive down here felt like jumping the divide in America. Expectations were in turn met, exceeded, and, in both cases, surprising. Trucks and cowboys, BBQ and burritos, everything was as I imagined, now real, with both charm and affront. This was the heartland: fat white clouds, intense thunderstorms, paddocks filled with cattle around ponds. This is what I wanted. The nostalgia for something I'd never experienced, holding onto it as it slips away. To be dirty and working hard in this quiet, bee-peppered glade: alive, completely alive.

When Danny parked the truck, I grabbed my veil from the back seat. The still-lit smokers hung on the back of the truck added a haze to the air. We both suited up, preparing for the final round of the day.

11

Texas Flip

2009

I arrived to find the shop enshrouded in a spooky morning fog. We had parked the truck a short twelve hours earlier with the relief of having finished a long day, but seeing the stack of detritus gathered during yesterday's clean-up run was a gut-punch reminder about the open-ended slog that lay ahead.

The truck's bed, from cab to license plate, was covered in old bee junk: rotten pallets, broken supers, heaps of comb mangled by wax moth, and even a pair of living hives with big, red X's spray-painted on them. This scarlet letter meant the hive was infected with American foulbrood, an incurable bacterial infection, though they had been surviving with it for who-knows-how-long. These hives were tucked into the middle of the junk because, instead of reorganizing at every yard, we had just piled a bit further on the back and then cinched them down with ropes and a prayer. We made it back to the shop without incident, though we probably wouldn't have survived a rutted back road or the scrutiny of a state trooper. The Bobcat, sitting in its trailer behind the truck, also looked like it could use a few more hours of sleep.

At our morning round-up—eight of us standing on the dirt parking area outside the workshop—each team received their daily orders. The crew of feisty Mexican women took their normal queen-catching duty, Susan and Binford would tend the breeders and cell builders, and my team, the package shakers, were heading across the county to put honey supers on a few yards. Before I could follow behind them, I had to empty the truck then load supers. This was fine by me: it meant a slow warm-up, stopping for a cup of coffee on the road and not having to be crammed shoulder to shoulder in the stinky truck before heading straight into the day's business.

As the crew loaded the goose-neck trailer, I took off the pallet of salvageable equipment and put it on the loading dock. The future of everything else was in the fire. A quick check showed that all four of the Freightliner's tires were full of air, and then the engine turned over without fuss—a decent start to the day.

I turned out of the driveway and followed the country road in a large loop around the block, then came back onto the property at a locked gate which led to a large, ash-blackened clearing. After parking the truck and untying the ropes, I put on a veil, climbed into the Bobcat, and bumped it off the trailer. I set the pallet of living hives in the center of the pit and then used the other junk to build a small structure around it.

There was no cure for this disease and no way to get the spores out of old equipment—it needed to be destroyed. A piece of old comb became my torch, and I jammed into the center of the pile. The dry equipment caught quickly—beeswax makes good candles for a reason—and soon I had a growling bonfire.

I had once heard a theory about why smoke calms bees: they think a forest fire is approaching, so they eat as much of their stored honey as possible in case they have to flee, and with full stomachs they are unable to sting. Watching these living hives burn, the bees standing idly around the entrance as the flames licked the sides of their hive, I could see firsthand that this was not the case.

When the flames had passed their zenith, I climbed back into the Bobcat, lifted another pallet of junk twelve feet into the air, and then tipped it onto the fire in a satisfying crunch of wood, ash, and heat. With a new batch of fuel, the fire roared into an inferno. The timing of each additional pallet had to be precise or else the nearby trees, which were already a little fire-baked, would be the first step towards the whole farm catching aflame. The cantankerous (and decidedly non-native) Barry often said that this part of Texas could use a good brushfire. Though I agreed in spirit, I wasn't yet ready to be the one who caused it.

With the Freightliner's bed clear and the bonfire tapering, I drove back to the shop and parked on the bare dirt in front of the comb warehouse. Its overhead garage door was off the tracks again, and it took all my strength to pull it up to the exact spot—about twenty inches from the ground—where a good, solid kick could set the one mischievous wheel back on track. Inside the warehouse was a truly hellish place: a 30 x 30 x 30-feet grimy cavern with super stacked upon super stacked upon super. Each pallet held 60 supers—six on each level, stacked ten-high—with the pallets stacked up to three levels, creating a 33-story "building." If organized well, four buildings could fit across four deep, but this was rarely the case. Unloading comb was always at the tail-end of a seemingly endless day, at the hour when one's primary fixation was taking off the boots and setting the poor toes into fresh air. Inside these stacks, the deep comb mixed with honey supers, and foundation assimilated with plastic frames. The second story always sat slightly askew compared to the first, and the third even more askew, creating these decrepit, wobbling skyscrapers reaching up into the cobwebbed darkness.

A chemical smell overran the wax, and I tried not to breathe too much while in the room. Once a month, we dumped in some harsh stuff to eradicate wax moths, but this somehow still didn't kill the black widows, brown recluse spiders ("brown cooters", my Very Texan neighbor called them), and a whole horror show of other creepy crawlies that populated every dark crevice. I imagined that whatever survived these chemical dumps was slowly evolving into a super predator that would one day rule the world. It was not a place to be working without a set of thick gloves.

I unloaded the Bobcat from the trailer, brought it inside, and surveyed my task. Another problem: this was a job meant for a forklift, not a Bobcat. A forklift picks up pallets vertically, while the Bobcat's arms lift at a fluctuating angle. Unfortunately, we didn't have a forklift—we had a Bobcat—and it required an extra level of focus and coordination to tilt the forks simultaneously and keep the pallet with untethered towers of supers level. Close to the ground this was easy, but a quick, applied geometry lesson showed the tilt of the forks changed dramatically the higher they went in the air. Also, the space was too small for

63

the Bobcat, and the cluttered, collected junk on the floor made it even smaller. Two pallets of supers would be easy to take out, I saw, but another sat at an awkward angle on the third story, while the fourth was currently unseen and would require some Tetris-like maneuvering to discover. I pushed the forks of the skid-steer inside the first pallet, sitting on the second level seven feet off the ground, and gingerly backed out.

While putting the first two pallets on the Freightliner, another pallet was revealed in the hidden column. This alleyway was too narrow for the Bobcat to pass through, and I needed to move one whole building—twenty-something feet high—a stride to the left. While it was possible to do this, I knew from hard experience that pushing a stack of two pallets had a much better chance of success than pushing three. I took off the uppermost pallet and put it on the ground outside. When I angled the Cat's prongs so they covered as many supers on the bottom pallet as possible, I slowly pushed the two-stack pallet to the left, scrutinizing the supers fifteen feet up in the air for the smallest wobble. They shifted smoothly. It was not my first pallet-moving party.

Actually, I thought to myself, I was getting pretty good at this. After months of practice, the Bobcat had grown into an extension of my body. I was able to sneak in the narrow channel I created, lift off the proper pallet and back out with a few spare inches on either side. After placing it on the truck, I returned into the warehouse for the final pallet on the ground—a victory lap. But with the finish line in sight, I let my guard down. Backing out of the warehouse a little too fast, I felt the back wheels drop, followed by a wave of forward momentum.

"Oh... NO." I groaned and froze, but my fear was confirmed by a BANG! ... BANG!BANG!BANG! The lip between the concrete floor and the dirt was a two or three-inch drop which deepened with every traverse. Going over it at any speed faster than a creep meant a strong jolt to the load. I had failed the final test. Cutting the engine, I lifted the safety bar and climbed out. Nearly four columns had fallen off the pallet and the supers laid in a chaotic heap of wood and wax. Somehow, and this always seemed to happen, every fallen comb had jumped out of its box. There was no easy way to put them back in. One at a time, nine per box, dozens of boxes.

I looked at the disorder in front of me. Thus far my morning consisted of burning a few thousand bees and moving junk around with a Bobcat. A beekeeper needs to do all of these chores, but some days I sure didn't feel like one.

12

Texas Gold

2009

I threw my entire weight against the 55-gallon drum to tilt it onto the dolly and then gave it another long shove to push it in motion. Wheeling it to the other drums of honey on the loading dock, twelve of them, I marveled at the harvest. Each drum weighed over 650 lbs. A single bee harvests a small amount of honey during her short life. After progressing though a series of tasks, her final job is to forage for nectar: she flies to a patch of flowers, fills her crop with nectar, and then bee-lines it back to the hive. She will continue gathering nectar until she is eaten by a predator, or her wings tatter, or she falls to the ground, too weak to fly. It was an admirable trait, I thought. Find something that you love and helps your community, and then fly until your wings wear out.

Arriving in the hive, the foragers transfer the nectar to another bee before returning to the air. The receiving worker collaborates with other bees to regurgitate and digest the honey, which adds enzymes and lowers the water content, before she deposits it in a cell. At night, the bees collectively flap their wings to create an air current inside the hive to reduce the moisture content of the nectar to below 18%, where natural yeasts are no longer active and will stay edible indefinitely. This is what we call honey. It is the bees' carbohydrate which they store in great quantity to eat when there are no natural sources of food, like during winter. It gives them the energy to shiver, which creates warmth inside their huddled cluster, and keeps the queen alive. In the early spring, the stored honey powers foragers to gather pollen—protein needed to raise new bees—and more nectar, which they will once again turn into honey.

If it is a good year (meaning the weather conditions are proper for melliferous plants) in a suitable location (some areas are good for honey production, others not), the bees will make more honey than they need to survive the winter and the beekeeper can harvest it for his or her pleasure. In olden times, harvesting honey meant destroying the hive; a natural colony or one inside a skep or a log is a maze of honeycomb, and the only way to harvest the honey was to tear apart the nest and flush out the colony. Around 150 years ago a beekeeper named L.L. Langstroth harnessed the concept of "bee space"—around one-fifth of an inch—which bees will use as a passageway and not fill with additional comb. If bees are given rows of straight wooden frames and a thin layer of beeswax at this precise dimension, they will build within this polite framework instead of the normal, free-for-all warren. Thus, we are now able to take out a frame and examine the eggs and larvae, move it to a different hive, or bring it back to the shop and extract its honey.

The final step is extra beneficial: instead of crushing the comb and letting the honey drip out, a frame is put in a giant centrifuge, spun at a high speed, and the honey flung out with minimal damage to the structure. The empty frame can be put back in the hive, and though the bees might be confused about where their harvest went, they will clean up the mess and fill it again without a noticeable complaint. Most importantly, they don't have to expend effort in building comb every year. With it taking approximately eight pounds of honey to build one pound of comb, this makes beekeeping much more productive. The beekeeper harvests the extra honey to eat and sell. In a large commercial operation with thousands of hives, this can result in the production of many barrels of honey.

I had spent the past hour on the final step of this process: pouring honey into drums. The empty barrels were stacked outside the warehouse in a lawless mixture of serviceable equipment and junk, and every subsequent barrel required a bit of shifting and searching to find all the necessary attributes: metal without rust or defects, a well-sealing top, and a latch with a bolt and screw. Barrel top number thirteen required an extra-deep rummage, but when it appeared under a pile of boxes, I headed back inside for the fun part: putting the barrel under the spout, opening the valve, and letting a two-inch stream of gold splash down. With my hands on the rims of the barrel, I stood mesmerized trying to imagine the number of flowers and bees that contributed to this growing vat of honey before me.

Perhaps a little too mesmerized. In a dazed moment, the socket wrench slipped from my hand and plopped into the pool of honey. The barrel was around two-thirds full, and, without thought, I immediately dunked my hand inside to grab the wrench. The honey's viscosity slowed the tool's descent, and on my second swipe I pulled out a dripping, yellow lump which shone under the florescent lights. My arm, up to the elbow, was also coated in this shine, and the honey quickly gave in to gravity and started to form rivulets down my hand and forearm. What could I do? Wash this bounty down the drain? No way, I thought, and I began to lick. I cleaned every inch of my arm that my tongue could reach—from a few inches above my elbow to in between my fingers—until only a sticky residue remained. My taste buds sung in a blazed-out glory.

After topping that barrel and rolling it to join the others, I went back outside to search for more components. I could see one good specimen at the bottom of a barrel pyramid, and I began tossing off the junk barrels like a video game character digging for a bonus life. I lifted one barrel over my head, the sugar rush peaking in my veins, and practically yelled to the gods. I must have sucked down two pounds of honey in a few minutes. A 55-gallon drum relative to my size might be the same ratio as a half-teaspoon to a bee. I was ready to fly.

13

Texas Lost

2009

We had something of a geographical problem in our operation.

Firstly, there was a regular phone book of locations—probably more than fifty—with around half of them hosting bees at any one time. After working in Texas for two seasons, the names had become more familiar, and I eventually learned that to get to the "Big Bend" yard, I needed to take a left at the junction of Route 180, followed by another quick left, then pass through three (not two!) gates, and turn after the big mimosa tree, skirt the pond, and I would soon see a grove with a collection of buzzing, white pillboxes. But with one missed turn or mixed detail in that series, I would spend the next half-hour driving around the property, or someone else's property, or a near-by town with every gate looking slightly more familiar than the last, and every goddamn big tree looking like a mimosa, whatever the hell that was. If, after that wasted thirty minutes, I still couldn't find the pond or the grove, it meant a fun call with Binford and a conceptual swap of geographical descriptions until he'd pop a bulb and tell me I was thinking of the "Underbrush" yard, which had the big mimosa tree, while at "Big Bend" I had to go through one gate, turn at the broken car, and go straight until I couldn't go straight anymore.

Binford was often more of the problem than the solution in these episodes. His directions shined both in their specificity and disregard for those wise to the scene. A few of his lines became instant classics. Once, he gave Susan instructions to turn at the old schoolhouse. She drove up and down the road several times looking for an old schoolhouse but found nothing that resembled it. Finally, it dawned on her that she was supposed to turn where the old schoolhouse used to be. Some thirty years earlier, it had been torn down and was currently an auto parts store. Another time he told Barry: go here, here and here, then turn left at the black church. As with Susan, the directions proceeded smoothly until the black church part, and Barry drove up and down the road until he too realized: a church with black parishioners. He later called up Binford in a huff: "It wasn't Sunday morning. How the hell would I know who goes to what church?"

More than once did I suffer from such abstractions. "After a goodly while," Binford described, "turn left onto a dirt road, pass the small forest on the left, and then take the first gate after you see cows in a field." My mind, preoccupied with filing the different terms into my mental cabinets, wouldn't consider what Binford had actually said until I began looking for the left turn onto the dirt road. Only then would I realize he'd described just about every back road in Texas. But on second thought, without a GPS, how else would one designate the way?

When driving a pickup truck, it's not much of a problem if you take a wrong turn or two. It's easy to scope out a dirt road to see if the "cows in a field" were just visiting the water tank en masse, or plain missing, redefining the directions into "turn into the first gate after the field". But when dragging a gooseneck trailer or, heaven forbid, driving the

two-ton Freightliner with a Bobcat behind it, an easy-going slip of direction can turn into a byzantine vehicular struggle.

I faced this problem on one pit-sweating Texas afternoon, nosing the Freightliner down a narrow back road while trying to find a yard I had never been to with forty-odd hives on the truck bed. I passed one or two gates which could have been my turn, but instead followed my gut and pushed ahead. Coming around the bend I saw a T-intersection, and my heart sank. Though sometimes a bit daffy with his instructions, I trusted Binford would not have failed to mention something as fortuitous as a T-intersection. With culverts on both sides and no possible turn around, I could only move forward. Every standstill moment meant more bees flying out of the hive—once again I had forgotten or didn't take time to put nets over the hives. I swallowed my spittle and turned right, which appeared to be a driveway, and soon I bumped into a dirt clearing with a house, a tree, a rope hanging from the tree, a tire laying on the ground beneath the rope, and a variety of rusting vehicles scattered about. Connected to the house was a slanted porch with two fine elderly specimens sitting upon it. My heart began to thump. I had to turn around this forty-foot truck and trailer, with live, stinging bees flying out of it, in this man's driveway, which was also his front yard, while he and his kin watched me.

As an opener I gave a friendly wave, which wasn't acknowledged, and then I pulled forward to initiate a simple K-turn. Of course the trailer immediately jackknifed—a long truck and tiny trailer are a tough turn—and a dirty panic coiled around my bones. Without the wind coming through the windows, I was helpless against that bastard of a sun, and sweat began pulsing out of me. I pulled forward again, and then over-adjusted the trailer into a jackknife the opposite way. With the truck relatively still, the bees began jumping out of the hives and looked for someone to blame for the strange afternoon of banging and jostling.

"GRRRRRRRR!" I groaned through my clenched teeth, which I tried to twist into a nonchalant smile for those observing. After committing the second error I give the porch-sitters my best "I'm sorry" wave and tried again. The air wasn't reaching the bottoms of my lungs and ball lightning arched across my skin. "Bees, please don't sting them," I prayed. "Sting me, sting me as much as you want, but don't sting those nice men. This isn't your new home. I didn't mean to bring you into their godforsaken holler. I want nothing to do with it."

Pull forward, reverse, jackknife. Pull forward, reverse, jackknife. The buzzing around the truck grew deeper.

"Please," I said, taking a deep breath and summoning all the coordination that ever was, or ever will be. When I glanced into the side mirror I saw a roughly-bearded man with sweaty hair plastered to his forehead and a look in his eye that would crack teeth. Is that me? I wondered. I was suddenly the spitting image of the insane man on my driver's license, the one my friends laughed about and said looked like the early portrait of a serial killer. "Look at what the Texan DMV did to me," I said at the time. Now I saw it only took a year of this southern swamp-heat for the dirty dregs to rise to the surface. Maybe it was time to get out of Texas, I thought to the rear view mirror.

Breaking eye contact, I focused on the trailer. On this attempt I somehow slipped the Bobcat between their water tank and a car raised up on blocks, allowing me a straight shot out the driveway. I gave the men on the porch one final wave, but they still didn't respond. I don't think they moved the entire time I was there. For all I knew, this bit of front-yard action could have been the most exciting thing to happen to them in weeks.

Back at the T-intersection, I stopped the truck and put my head on the steering wheel. My mouth tasted of hot, rusted tin. I could see bees crawling on the back of my eyelids. I thought about making a run for the border: cutting the ropes and blowing town, with the hives careening off the back as I whipped around turns, a fleet of yelping Texans in their trucks hot on my tail.

The daydream shattered. It was time to unload these bees somehow and somewhere. I confronted the situation the only way I knew how: drive forward, stop at every locked gate, and check if our key fit one of the locks on the chain. On the third or fourth stop, I felt the click of the padlock in my hands, and relief came in droves. I would finish this day. I drove to the nearest piece of level ground, offloaded the pallets, and climbed back into the truck without getting a single sting.

14

Hawaii Paradise

2010

Hawaii is a paradise, or so they say. Its reputation is planted deep within our collective consciousness: Hawaii is a playground for the privileged, a vacationland for honeymooners, a magic island where it is a constant 86° F, where you can go swimming with dolphins in January, where exotic fruits drop from trees, and the smell of plumeria flows into your nostrils unimpeded. Hawaii is the preferred fantasy destination for everyone lifting their head on a gray November afternoon in Camden, Delaware, and wondering if the freezing rain will turn into sleet. Paradise waits at the end of that daydream. Daydreams never include a rotten shadow. Daydreams never have back pain.

I pick up the stool, carry it five feet and set it on the jagged black lava rocks. Once these were a mass of hot magma flowing towards the sea, but now they are the cracked and jumbled bedrock of the entire island. They can easily shift underfoot, especially when you and three other people are each holding the corner of a plugged, three-deep hive, stumbling backwards while getting stung, and I blame my current knee pain from a single misstep a month prior. I give the nuc's entrance a puff of smoke, sit on the stool, and take off the lid.

The nuc is the size of a shoebox. The inside is divided by a wooden plank and two miniature colonies, around two hundred bees in each, coexisting in a duplex. I send a delicate puff of smoke along the top bars, not so much to send the bees running into the corners but enough to deter any guards from an immediate sting to my face. Somewhere in each small colony is a newly-mated queen bee. Using my hive tool I separate the combs and lever one out. Hundreds of workers crawl on its face, but I see her, their mother, standing blank steady on a newly lain patch of eggs. Eggs mean success—she has mated and is ready to sell—and I pick her up by the thorax with a well-practiced delicacy. Using a sawed-off nail, I dot her back with blue model paint. She is now easier to see, and the blue color will let beekeepers know what year she was born. The queen's legs writhe in confusion, her mandibles open and close in silent protest. I dry the paint by blowing on it, and then point her headfirst into a matchbox-sized cage between my knees.

One would think Hawaii is also a paradise for bees and their keepers. The Kona side of the Big Island is a sliver of the Mediterranean climate in the South Pacific, meaning most often it is hot and dry but still has enough rain to keep plants alive, so there is something flowering all year long. This is the perfect zone for queen breeding, a business where rain is the number one enemy. Rain prevents queens from going on their mating flight. Breeders are beholden to the pupation cycle of a queen bee, and there is a neat and tidy train-line schedule where queen cells—pupating queen bees—need to be in a nuc before they hatch, and the nuc's queen needs to be mated and captured before the cells goes in. This means if there are multiple days of rain in a row, young queens are unable to fly and mate, and the queen cells will start hatching before there is any place to put them. Money, some twenty dollars per queen, starts flowing down the lava tube. This is why queen breeders flock to the Kona rather than Hilo side of the Big Island, which gets some of the most rainfall of anywhere in the US Only a giant, sacred, sometimes snow-capped mountain separates the two locations.

There are eight of us in the yard. We are bee workers: picking up our stools and putting them down, opening, smoking, cursing, catching, caging, scraping, closing. Over a thousand hives are within eye shot, far too many for the surrounding flowers to support. Instead the bees live on sugar syrup and protein patties from China. In the box attached to my catching stool, I already have forty queens adjusting to their wooden prisons. By the end of the day, I'll have caught over a few hundred. They have no concept of how far they will travel in the next week.

When I finish one row, I pick up my stool and move to the next. This round I sit next to Phil, a reptile-loving metalhead, tall and bald with a serious pair of muttonchops, the friendliest guy in the world until you flip his switch in the wrong direction. As usual, we begin to talk about music—this time we dig a little deeper into one of his favorite bands— The Residents—while our hands go through the motions of catching and caging queens. Phil gets stuck looking for a virgin queen, and I push forward, soon working alongside Jake, a goateed Oregonian who had just recently arrived on the island with his wife and three children. We pick up a conversation about surfing and body-boarding from a dozen rows earlier, and he chastises me because I hadn't yet rode a wave even though I have been living in Hawaii for months. No time, I tell him. One row up Jaelyn flies by, finishing three nucs in the time it takes us to do two. The first days of catching queens I tried to race my co-workers down each row to see if I could catch the most queens in a day. After a week of rushing and mistakes, I eased into a slow-but-steady pace that I realized most of the crew had already perfected.

Queen breeders caught onto this idea of Hawaiian weather in the 1960s. Queens are bred and raised in the Hawaiian sun and sent back to the mainland. The queens, each in their own cage, are put by the dozens in a box with mesh sides with worker bees added in the interspace to cluster around and care for the queens on the journey. This buzzing box gets put into the mail system and will be shipped at high speed to anywhere in North America: California, Montana, Florida, Alberta, Minnesota.

Beekeepers who truck thousands of hives thousands of miles across the US also order thousands of queens from Hawaii each year. Requeening, a common practice for commercial beekeepers, is the killing of the current queen and introduction of a new one. A hive with a two-year old queen is potentially weaker and more susceptible to diseases; she is no longer as fertile and productive as she was in her first year. A queen can live for several years, but the bees will eventually kill her themselves and raise a new one. Commercial beekeepers will skip the slow colony decline, unpredictable mating process, and three lost weeks of production during which a colony raises a new queen, and in-

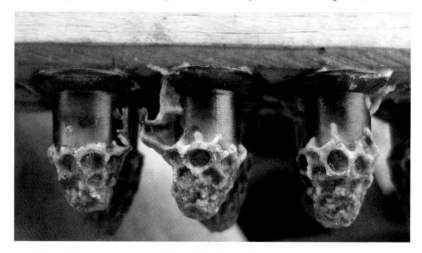

stead purchase a queen and do the dirty deed themselves. If you have a thousand hives, a full set of queens can knock some $15,000 a year out of your budget, but the cost is generally seen as worthwhile. Some people think this process is appalling—causing the premature death of a queen for the sake of production—but it is something the bees, ever the efficiency experts themselves, already do quite readily. There is no humanity residing within the hive walls, and colony survival is the number one priority.

Probably more horrible from the queen's perspective is the caging period and journey across the Pacific. Here, she is packed together with dozens of other queens, all emitting strong pheromones which likely drive each other crazy. There is only one queen bee in each hive, but when honey bees need to produce a new queen, they raise a dozen or more for a better chance that one successfully hatches. Each queen comes into the world with one thing on her mind: kill the other queens. The first one that emerges systematically travels through the hive and stings the other queen pupae through the wax cell walls as they are mere hours or minutes away from emerging themselves. If another has already hatched, the two new queens will fight to the death. In our manufactured shipping scenario, they are kept in close quarters for a few days, trapped, confused, driven to kill each other, but unable to do anything but run around in their 1x2 inch cages.

There are several queen breeders based around Kona—giant operations with tens of workers and thousands of hives. I am working for one of them for a season. I haven't heard any official numbers, but my outfit can produce somewhere around three hundred thousand queens in a single year. In the breeders' bullpen they have about two dozen breeder queens which are selected mostly for their traits in hon-

ey production and color. It would be much better to select for pest and disease resistance, but because there are still chemicals in the market that work against these foes, beekeepers can still focus on superficial traits like the queen's golden color. Some of the best queens out there are scrawny little runts, but as with much in this life, image can stretch a lot longer than performance. This also means that three hundred thousand queens spread about North America each year are descendants from only this handful of mothers. That is a frightening genetic bottleneck.

We, the eight of us working the yard, are a small cog in this chain. Stung and sweating—another hive, another queen, another hive, another queen, another sting, another puff of smoke, another hive, another queen—we work in industrial beekeeping. A few days into a work week, I am stumbling across the lava rocks in a mechanized daze. Another hive, another queen; here's one that is a bit too dark and small to sell. She's a wild hatch, not a first generation from the top breeder queens, and I feel her exoskeleton crunch between my fingertips. When I drop the carcass into the hive, a few bees take notice and gather around her. I still don't know if I believe in insect sadness— or pain—but the bees will spend twenty minutes around their dead queen, touching and tasting her before dragging the body outside the hive and dumping it on the rocks. In another twenty minutes her pheromone will disperse, and they will focus their energies on raising their next mother.

The days are long. The job is dull. But good does emerge. At any point of the day, I can see the ocean-blue cover one direction and a worthy mountain in the other. The temperature is pitch-perfect, with friendly clouds rolling in after lunch just as the sun threatens to get too hot. Every day I snag fresh fruit from a bee yard: mango, paradise fruit, papaya, and avocado all grown in the wild. The bees are absurdly calm. Instead of wearing a suit of body armor as I did in Texas, I work without gloves, sometimes without a veil, and my work outfit consists of torn jeans and an offensive Hawaiian shirt. At the end of the shift, I ease out of my work boots, put on my sandals, and throw whatever fruit I gathered that day in a blender with some ice and rum. Then, I take my concoction to the shore, a five-minute walk away, and play old sea shanties on my concertina while the sun sets. Sometimes, there are dolphins splashing about, and, once, a whale breached as the sun crashed into the ocean. With the palate of colors deepening and the lulling sound of the waves against the rocks, I look around and say to myself: this is the true ending of a day. This is alright.

Then, the sun sets. I go back to the bunkhouse, toss together a quick meal, and fall asleep on the couch in my work clothes. The next morning I am again at the shop, bright and early, lighting my smoker. We drive to a yard, 8:15 AM, my co-workers already lighting up bowls of weed to push them into the day. We take our catching stools and disperse to the rows of nucs. We stand up, move, sit down. We chat, we complain, we gossip. Queen catching becomes automatic, thoughtless motions punctuated by a sting every now and again. I don't often consider the apples or almonds these bees will help create. When I finish one row of hives, I pick up the stool, march down the line and start the next. The morning isn't half over. A husky, red-faced Kentucky boy named Adam—like me, here just for the season—plunks his stool on the row next to mine. Sitting down, his plumber's crack is visible to half the world. We work without talking, lost in thought and the steady buzz of flying bees. About half-way through the row Adam turns to me, wipes the sweat off his brow, and tells me he is thinking of becoming a wedding photographer.

When I talk to people back on the mainland, they will inevitably say something like, "Gosh, it was 10° F. here this morning," a hint of jealousy in their voices. "How's Hawaii?"

I'm not sure how to answer. I often say, "It's not quite paradise."

15

Turkey Quest

2010

✽

The van passed me without slowing down. In fact, it might have sped up when it saw me, and I reflexively took a step further off the road. Without a hint of brake lights, the vehicle whipped around the corner, and I was left alone with a hillside of trees and rocks. The road was narrow and bordered by steep cliffs as it squeezed into the valley alongside a river. With no traffic I could only hear the bubbling of water over the rocks, and I resumed my pacing back and forth. I had traveled far to be here, and my goal was tantalizingly close. But was this how the journey would end? A pacing, crazed tramp on the side of a nameless foreign road?

It was, I realized, not far from the truth. If any of my friends and family were questioned as to my whereabouts, the most informed answer they could give would be Eastern Turkey. I only had enough money on me for one more night in a cheap hotel and a bus ticket to get back to Istanbul, which was over six hundred miles away. In the face of this, there seemed to be only one answer: to accept defeat and retreat. However, by this point I had relinquished most logic and was driven by something even I couldn't understand. The noisy river tumbled over the rocks and splashed happily towards the sea. It had its goal, and I had mine. I sat down on my lumpy backpack and studied the hillside once again. I told myself that I had a good feeling the next car would be my ride.

Ten days earlier, I had arrived in Istanbul to find an article in the city's newspaper which, approximately translated, said this:

"On the Anzer Plateau in the district of Rize, it was announced at the Honey, Culture and Tourism Festival that the price of the famous Anzer honey is 550 Turkish lira per kilogram this year. Last year the honey sold at 500 Turkish lira per kilogram. This season the harvest began on August 15th, and, if the weather conditions are suitable, they expect to have 700 pounds of Anzer honey this season."

550 lira per kilo? At first I thought my Turkish friend had made a mistake in translation or that my jet-lagged brain had not nailed down the currency exchange. With 1.5 Turkish lira to a dollar, this Anzer honey sold at about US $366 per kilo, or $166 per pound. A pound of honey for $166 dollars. I made her read it again, took out a pencil and a piece of paper and did the math once more. There was no mistake. A pound of honey for $166 dollars.

This figure set my imagination aflame. The luxury, the ... audacity of this Anzer honey. Images of honey production from around the world ran through my head: bees collecting the nectar and ripening it into honey, beekeepers pulling the honey off, running the hot knife over

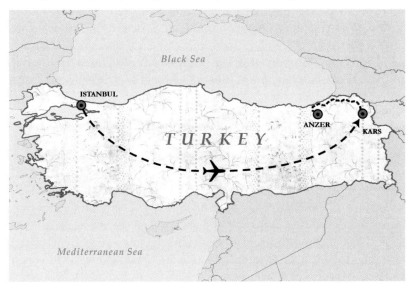

the caps and spinning the frames in the extractor. All through this process drops of honey are spilled, eaten, smeared, wasted, lost. How would it change if each drop was worth its weight in gold? Gold, I soon checked, was slightly dearer than Anzer honey, but Anzer did compare economically to Tellurium, a chemical element (#52) that is used in alloy production. Also, it seems that one could swap a kilo of Anzer honey for a kilo of ivory from a woolly mammoth skeleton buried in Siberia and come away clean.

The previous "most expensive" honey I knew was Manuka honey from New Zealand. It is a dark, strong-flavored honey, and there is much ado about its medicinal properties. By the time the Manuka reaches the shelves, at least the Internet's shelves, it sells for about $40 a pound. Then there is the rare, white Kiawe honey from Hawaii, produced only in small amounts from a certain grove of trees on the Big Island. Both sell for prices that aren't exactly easy on the budget but nothing as jaw-dropping as the Anzer honey from Turkey.

I needed to learn more about Anzer honey. A few Turkish websites sold the honey online, many of them claiming that they were the only true Anzer honey providers and that the other online stores were liars and thieves. These websites were decorated with kitschy photos and unsubstantiated health benefit claims. One website had a list of twenty-eight grave ailments that Anzer honey has been clinically shown to cure. These included (phrases unaltered): "Destroy arteriosclerosis and vein hardness, Treats cancer illness in early diagnosis, Destroys tonsil infection, Support growing, Improves brain illness and paralysis, Gives power to memory, Whets the appetite, Disappears constipation, Disappears barren, Prevents loss of hair, Treats hepatit b,c, Disappears weakness, and Increases sexual power." It seemed to be a true panacea.

The only scientific research I could find on Anzer honey was a paper entitled, "Protective Effect of Anzer Honey Against Ethanol-Induced Increased Vascular Permeability in the Rat Stomach," in the journal *Experimental and Toxicologic Pathology*. The research indicates that "Anzer honey is able to protect the stomach of the rat against ethanol-induced increased vascular permeability, which may be correlated with the ascorbic acid content." It looked like the field was wide open for future Anzer honey scientists.

Yet after skimming off the surface of health-benefit-propaganda, I soon found that consuming Anzer honey could be downright dangerous. The honey comes from *Rhododendron ponticum*, a plant that is native to the hilly Pontus region of eastern Turkey. Rhododendrons are highly toxic plants, producing a grayanotoxin in the leaves and flower nectar. The toxins create a poisonous honey. Usually, toxic honey is not a problem because there normally aren't giant fields of the flower for monofloral production.

The nectar is even toxic to the bees, probably disabling or killing them before they can amass any grayanotoxin-flavored honey. Cases of Mad Honey Disease (formally known as Honey Intoxication by the US Food and Drug Administration) are practically non-existent in the US. In Turkey, however, the bees in the Pontus region have supposedly evolved a resistance to the *R. ponticum*'s toxin and are able to subsist on this "deli bali", or mad honey. The few recent cases of Mad Honey Disease, or "Chronic Mad Honey Intoxication", have been reported in Turkey. These were patients who ate non-commercial honey daily and reported symptoms such as slow heart rate or atrioventricular conduction abnormalities. Their illness was easily remedied by the cessation of honey consumption.

Historically there are some tall tales about this Mad Honey. In the 17th century it was produced in tons and sent around the Mediterranean to be quaffed with ale for a bit more kick in one's drink. There are even stories of the honey used as a chemical weapon of sorts. According to the chronicle Anabasis, in 401 B.C. the Greek army under Xenophon decided to raid some local hives on their trek back from a successful campaign in Persia. After consuming the honey as a pillager might, the soldiers suffered fits of intoxication and immobilization. From Xenophon's writings:

"The effect upon the soldiers who tasted the combs was that they all went for the nonce quite off their heads and suffered from vomiting and diarrhea with a total inability to stand steady on their legs. A small dose produced a condition not unlike violent drunkenness, and a large [dose] caused an attack very like a fit of madness—some dropped down, apparently at death's door. So they lay, hundreds of them, as if there had been a great defeat, a prey to the cruelest despondency. But the next day, none had died; and almost at the same hour of the day at which they had eaten they recovered their senses, and on the third or fourth day got on their legs again like convalescents after a severe course of medical treatment."

Having second thoughts about ordering that Anzer honey with your ale?

Another notable incident, detailed by the Greek geographer and historian Strabo in his book "Geography" occurred a few centuries later. In 67 B.C. the Roman general Pompey and his troops were at war with King Mithridates of Pontus, with the Romans at great advantage troop-wise and Mithridates retreating. Along the road, Mithridates' army left potfuls of the mad honey which the Romans feasted upon in their victorious march. After eating the honey, the Romans went into helpless convulsions and Mithridates' army took advantage and massacred over a thousand of the troops.

My curiosity was burning. I wanted to discover what a $10 drop of honey tasted like and see with my own eyes the fields of rhododendrons high up in the mountains. I found the town of Anzer on a map; it was small, out of the way, and on the opposite side of Turkey. A small detail. I could fly to Kars, in Eastern Turkey, and then make my way back to Istanbul over land. This region of Turkey, from Kars to Rize, is one of the country's biggest honey-producing areas, and I figured I would taste my way through the countryside until I came upon the final, ultimate flavor of the Anzer honey. What would happen? What would the Anzer honey taste like? Would I go mad? Would I be able to afford enough to go mad? These were dangers of honey tasting I had never had to consider, but my palate was ready.

A few days later I was in the Istanbul airport. I was excited, and I was ready. Anzer, here we come. Then the wheels came off the wagon.

Excited may have been too strong a term; hungover and sleep-deprived was a more accurate description of my state. It had been a long, strange night of Karaoke with my Turkish friend Dunya in some multi-story bar in Taksim. On the bus to the airport, in the harsh, early-morning light, it dawned on me that only a few hours earlier I had been singing a Johnny Cash song in Spanish in Turkey. I stood at the airport's ATM and undertook the formidable task of understanding and then counting the play-money that it had just spit out at me. People, looking much fresher than I, were bustling to-and-fro. The announcer said something over the PA system. My head hurt. The ATM was beeping at me. I was counting. My debit card sat in the blinking slot, asking me to pick it up and put it in my wallet. Nearly at the end of my stack of bills, I then saw, out of the corner of my eye, my debit card getting sucked back into the machine like a slurping strand of pasta. And gone. Nothing. Not there. The machine had eaten my card.

I pressed buttons. I slapped the side of the machine. A half-yelp, half-squeak emitted from my throat. My flight was in thirty minutes. I found a phone number on the machine and called it, but the person at the other end of the line only spoke Turkish. I ran to the other side of the terminal where the bank had a branch, but they couldn't do anything for me. There was no way I was going to get my card back, and I didn't have any other means to get more money. My only economic backing was the cash I had taken out of the machine just then. If I boarded the plane, that cash was going to have to keep me going until I ordered another card, which would have to be mailed to Istanbul.

The strangeness of the situation swamped me. The fragility and ethereal nature of digital currency became very real as soon as all the money I had access to was on my person. Crossing paths with one pickpocket would reduce me to a frighteningly natural state. On top of this, I was heading to a rural region where not many people spoke English, and I spoke no Turkish. The only words I knew were *bal* (honey), *arı* (bee) and *arıcı* (beekeeper) but my pronunciations were laughable. The safe option was to retreat to my friend's house and spend a week on borrowed money until I got a new card. Though the anger and frustration had momentarily clouded my brain, my curiosity was still a bright light in the background. After a pace up and down the terminal, I sent a little prayer for better luck and boarded the airplane.

By the time we landed in Kars, I was calmer and of sound mind (and perhaps less hungover). I had figured out a plan. If I stuck to a shoe-string budget, I would be able to get to Anzer on my way back to Istanbul in time to get a new debit card, and then catch the train north to Slovenia, where I would be living and studying the next year. With the plan settled, the lump of worry in my gut softened, and I could focus on enjoying this foreign land and its honey.

Kars had a Wild West feeling to it. It was built by the Russians in a landscape that looked like barren Wyoming. Its pastel, stone buildings looked ready to stand against a severe, high-plains storm that could be coming soon, maybe even today. The town was tucked up against a castle-topped hill and barely crept onto the plain before abruptly giving way to a vast lowland of scrub grass and prickly plants.

It was a cloudy day when I arrived, and the combination of the yellow plains and gray skies made for a sickly color scheme. Pale mountains stood off in the distance. The area looked dry, but apparently it was a honey producing Mecca. The hillsides above town were dotted with one-story hives tucked in among the rocks. When I took a closer look at one patch of hives, I found the black Caucasian bees undeterred by the threatening weather. They continued to zip in and out of their hives in search of a fall nectar flow.

The honey from these hives was prominently displayed throughout downtown Kars. Shops dedicated solely to honey and cheese were on every corner; I counted over twenty of them in town. Honey and cheese being two of my favorite substances, I revised my earlier snap-judgments of Kars. The typical honey-cheese shop had frames of comb honey hanging in the window, giant wheels of cheese stacked around the shop, and jars of honey lining the shelves. I dedicated an entire afternoon walking from shop to shop, taste-testing their honeys and comparing prices and flavors.

I consider myself more of a honey fan than a connoisseur. I can taste the difference between, say, clover and chestnut honey, but when it comes to the subtleties of intra-monofloral tasting I am mostly helpless. I have no idea how honey judges can make their way through a competition tasting ten different honeys of the same variety but declaring only one the best. My palate freezes up after about the fifth honey and they all start to taste about the same on my sugar-saturated tongue. I do sometimes like to pretend, though, so I bounced from store to store in Kars and put on my best epicurean show.

In each shop I would make the international taste-testing sign (pointing at the jars of honey and then touching the tip of my tongue). After holding the jar to the light and inspecting its color, I would dip a small wooden stick into the honey and then go through all sorts of little sensory rituals while absorbing the honey on my tongue. Lots of lip-smacking, tongue-waggling and breathing in through my mouth while the salesman waited anxiously for my verdict (or more likely was annoyed). I would taste drop of honey through and through, thank the shopkeeper (*Teşekkürler* was another word I could summon about half of the time) but I would hold out on a purchase until I completed my full circuit to find the best honey of Kars.

My conclusions were thus: there were two types of honey in Kars. One was light, and one was dark. One came from the fields, the other came from trees. The best honey, according to my unofficial scorecard, happened to be from the shop where the owner could speak a little English, and we had a gesture-filled talk about beekeeping, America and basketball. Did that influence my decision? Probably. But he was a nice guy and gave me a good price on a small jar of his honey.

While the cheese and honey built me into a state of food rapture, I was still aware of every purchase. I continually evaluated my budget and realized that after the daily expenditures of a cheap hotel, bus fare and a little food, I did not have much honey money. As a backup plan I put enough lira for a bus ticket to Istanbul at the very bottom of my backpack where I could not get it confused with my daily allowance. Time was ticking. The next morning I repacked my bags and took a bus to Artvin.

As soon the bus cleared the Kars city limits, we swept into the empty plains. Shepherds idly looked over their flocks of cattle and sheep and turned their heads to watch the bus pass. Every twenty or thirty minutes we would pass through another village that seemed to spring out of the earth. These settlements consisted of a handful of stone houses surrounded by stone walls and were populated with people, dogs, chickens, sheep, and beehives. After a few hours of driving, the road crept into a stream gulch that flowed off the plains. I watched the landscape evolve into craggy, rugged box canyons, looking like I-70 on the west side of Colorado, except this was a narrow, windy, two-lane track. The rock was a muddy red and had some scrub brush and pine trees clinging in the crevasses of the lower valleys. For nearly eight hours I watched the mountains, and around every corner was a view of a world I never imagined. Somehow, for about five of those hours, I had the song, "Do you know the Muffin Man?" sometimes alternating with "The Wheels on the Bus" stuck in my head. I found myself chanting the lyrics under my breath. By the end of the ride, my mental deterioration was starting to overpower my ability to absorb the visual beauty.

Artvin was an attractive town clinging to a mountainside steep enough to have been a ski slope. The road hairpin-turned nine times to get from the river up to the center of town, which was only a barely-level two-block area. Then the mountain walls rose up again, with apartment buildings clinging to the earth at a strange angle. Artvin was less interesting from a beekeeper's standpoint, with only a few shops that sold a darker and flavorful local honey, but I had planned to make another jump from Artvin to the Camili valley on the Georgian border where there is a Caucasian queen-breeding program. The Camili valley is naturally secluded from any other strain of bee, making it a perfect breeding ground for pure Caucasian bees. Unfortunately, due to some Turkish-Georgian tensions, the government required a permit for foreigners to travel to the Camili valley, a permit that took two weeks to obtain. I had to nix this plan, and, after a day in Artvin, I pushed on.

To Rize! It was a partly-sunny, temperature-confusing morning when I arrived in Rize, a city with a population of almost one hundred thousand, built around a small bay on the Black Sea. The bus had driven along the coast for a few hours, and from my seat I watched dolphins splash in the waters to the right while workers harvested tea leaves on the steep hills to the left.

I spent nearly an hour wandering around Rize with my heavy pack, first just to see what the city had to offer, and second, to try to figure out how to get to Anzer. I soon found out that Anzer was not a popular destination, or even a known one. Even though it was only fifty or sixty miles away, people looked at me as if I was asking how to get to the moon. True, Anzer was a small town at the top end of a valley road with no thru-traffic, but there had to be a bus that went there, right?

There was no bus station in Rize. A line of minibuses gathered along one long road, each with a different number and destination written on its front. My search was fraught with confusion and miscommunication. I would walk up to someone who looked helpful and say to him "Anzer?" pointing at the buses. He would be confused until I pulled out my map and showed him the dot that was Anzer. This would clarify things, but he wouldn't be unable to answer me in English. Usually, he would call a friend over and discuss the question, pointing at the map, and then pointing in a direction with a few words in Turkish. I would thank him and head in that direction, no idea what he was trying to tell me. When I couldn't find Anzer written on a bus, I would repeat the entire process again, often finding my new guide pointing me in the opposite direction.

Frustration began to creep in. Finally, someone pointed me to a near-by minibus and motioned for me to join. We waited for the bus to fill. I was still unsure if this bus was even the right one, but, when every seat was occupied, the driver started the vehicle, and we crept out of Rize. Watching as we left town, my map skills told me that we were heading in the right direction and gave me a small measure of relief. My sitting neighbor offered me a pretzel and spoke a little English. He told me the bus was not going to Anzer, only to Ikizdere, which was about halfway. I was feeling good about my progress. My money supply was dwindling, but I had enough left in my wallet for another day or two, and now the goal was within reach.

It took a half hour to follow the river up to Ikizdere, and we passed many beehives and small honey stands along the ride. At the final stop I exited the bus with everyone else, blinking in confusion and trying to figure out what to do next. My pretzel-friend had delivered the bad news on the way up; when asked about Anzer, he emphatically told me, "No bus." I had taken this pronouncement lightly at first: it couldn't be true, there should be buses to everywhere. How could the local people get to their homes? But standing on the small, one-street town of Ikizdere, I somehow could tell there would be no bus to Anzer today. Or tomorrow. The man beckoned me to follow him, and, for lack of anything better to do, I did. Walking through Ikizdere, I did not feel uncomfortable, but as a tall foreigner with a large backpack, I definitely stood out among the townsfolk as they sold vegetables, drank tea or went about their daily business.

My friend brought me to modern four-story rectangular building on a road off the main street. We entered and walked up three sets of stairs to get to a room which held three people drinking tea. The one behind the desk, talking on the phone, looked official. I had no idea why I was in this place, but I sat down in a nearby chair. As soon as the man hung up the phone, my pretzel-friend addressed everyone in Turkish.

Suddenly they all turned their attention to me. The room was hot, and I started to sweat.

"Umm ... bus ... autobus to Anzer?" I asked. "No bus," the man behind the desk replied. He pointed at another man in the room. "Taxi," he said and then pointed at the desk, "Hotel." The confusion was cleared, slightly. There was no bus to Anzer. I either had to hire a taxi or stay in the hotel. My train felt derailed, and I tried to process this information while the rest of the people in the office tried to help me.

The man behind the desk wrote down a number on a scrap of paper and handed it to me: the price of a hotel room. The taxi driver made an offer to drive me to Anzer, but then another taxi driver appeared and made a better offer. They argued while I kept shaking my head and tried to think of how to explain myself. More people came into the office and attempted to translate my words. I could see all of them reaching back to their school lessons in English just to tell this dumb foreigner that he was way out of his league.

The final bid from one of the taxi drivers was 110 Turkish lira, which was more the twice my daily spending limit. The man behind the desk found Google Translate on the computer and gestured for me to come over. There were five people in the office now, all animatedly discussing my future in Turkish. The man behind the desk had translated the word "bargain" and pointed from the screen to the piece of paper with the number on it. He then clicked on the speaker button, and the female-robotic voice on the computer said, "Bargain," and when I didn't say anything he clicked it again and again. "Bargain ... bargain ... bargain." Did he want me to bargain with him or was his offer a bargain? I was completely at a loss for words. There was no air in the room, and my brain was on the fritz. "I don't ... I want ..." I said, but I didn't know what I wanted. The man switched Google Translate to 'English to Turkish' and motioned for me to type.

I looked at the keyboard. How do I explain this situation? How do I tell these people that I came all the way across the country with no money and only a few facts to get to this small village just so, for no great reason, I could see the place where this magical, dreadfully expensive honey was produced and just put a few drops on my tongue? The whole absurdity of the journey fell in a lump on top of me as I stared at the blinking cursor. All eyes in the room watched me, and I could feel the sweat beading on my forehead. Another person wandered into the room at this standoff, but he already seemed to know what was going on. Or maybe this sort of thing happened everyday around here. I typed in the first thing that crept into my head and stood up. The man at the computer read the screen and looked up at me in confusion: "I am the muffin man," it read. "Sorry," I said to the room. Then I picked up my bag, waved goodbye, and walked out the door.

I received no awards for improving international relations on this trip. The sauna-heat and the overwhelming confusion that filled that office was no place to think, and I needed to do some serious recalculating of options.

Once outside, the fresh air immediately improved my mental standing, and I was able to make some decisions. My first thought sent me walking north towards Anzer. It took only a few minutes before I was at the edge of town where a small market was set up along the road. Vendors gathered here and set up wooden tables underneath umbrellas to sell everything from whisks to onions. In the middle of the market, there were a couple of plastic jugs of honey proudly displayed on milk crates, and two women were crouched ten feet away in the shade of a building, waiting for customers. All the bees in the neighborhood had found these jugs and were hogpiling along the cap's cracks. I asked for the price of the jug, which looked like a kilo, and the woman held up all of her fingers: 10 lira, or six dollars. The honey was dark and had bee parts and bits of wax floating on top. I thanked her and kept on walking north, out of town.

After an hour of being ignored by cars and watching the mountains, there I was: on the side of a country road in eastern Turkey, hitchhiking, nearly broke, and with my goal tragically out of reach. When walking out of the hotel, I had a little daydream that someone would pick me up on the outskirts of town, telling me (in perfect English) that they just happened to be driving to Anzer, and, of course, they would love to give me a tour, host me for the night, and treat me to a taste of the Anzer honey. But this dream was setting with the sun behind the western mountains. I was pushed to the limit, mentally and financially. I had tried, and I had failed. It was time to head back to Istanbul and arrive with pennies in my pocket and my tail between my legs. But, as a final stand, I had convinced myself to wait for that one last car, and until that one last car drove past me, the dream was still alive.

A few purple flowers still showed some color on the side of the road. The bees had found them and were in a happy, foraging bliss, dipping their proboscises into the nectaries and sucking up that sweet liquid. I couldn't identify what plant they were working, but I knew it wasn't a rhododendron, which got me to thinking. If there happened to be a rhododendron sitting next to these flowers, which plant would the bees prefer?

Bees certainly care about their nectar source, preferring certain plants over others, but when only one species of plant exists within their range, they will forage on it, innocent of other possibilities. When you don't know what you don't have, you don't need it.

Watching these bees tumble between the flowers and fly heavily back to their hives, I couldn't help but smile. It was that newspaper article, that tidbit of information and its remarkable timing that had sent me all the way out here. Without that, where would I be? That question was mostly irrelevant; for me, the happiness of the recent adventure— the people I had met, the flavors I had tasted, and the sights I had seen—had vastly outweighed the overall goal. If these bees could be satisfied with that purple flower, then I could be as well.

The end of the rainbow was right in front of my nose all along, but trying to grasp it was like trying to catch that bee as it returned to its home laden down with nectar and pollen. At that thought, the weight fell off my back, and I made my decision. I picked up my bag and began walking towards town, downhill with the river, to the market and the thick, dark plastic jars of honey.

Back in Istanbul, after the overnight bus ride across the country and the recovery of my economic identity, I walked down the street a mere mile away from where I'd heard about Anzer honey and stumbled upon a shop with the name, "Bal Dünyasi & Şarküteri," or Honey World and Deli. Inside was a honey-lover's dream: jars upon jars of honey lining the walls, different colors and flavors from all over Turkey. I was as excited as ... well, as a beekeeper in a honey store. The man and the woman who ran the shop did not understand English, but I talked to them as if they did in a free associative ramble. The woman shadowed me around the store with a large calculator, punching in price numbers and speaking to me in loud, clear words, as if I might be able understand Turkish if she enunciated well.

Finally, the idea struck me. "Anzer honey, do you have Anzer honey?" I asked. All four eyebrows went up. I pointed to my tongue. The woman said something to the man and immediately ran out of the store while the man reached under the counter and brought out an oddly-shaped, tinfoil-covered jar labeled, "ANZER". Now I really had to laugh—the fabled honey that I had traveled across the country and gone through such ordeals to find was a mere walk from where I had started this adventure? Oh, well.

The woman returned to the store with a bottle of water in her hand for me. The tinfoil, the water ... if the man put on heavy duty rubber gloves and laboratory goggles, I would really begin to get nervous. The honey salesman carefully unwrapped the tinfoil and uncapped the jar. He gave me a small wooden stick, and I dipped it into the Anzer honey.

It was a dark, reddish liquid, and I held it up to the light. The woman was looking at me carefully and had the bottle of water already open. Smacking my lips and clearing my mouth of all other tastes, I thought of the tricked Romans, the convalescent Greek army, the permeable rat stomachs and the intoxicated bees on the Pontus plains. Then I stuck the honey in my mouth and pressed it firmly on my tongue.

16

Slovenia Switch

2011

"Furthermore, beekeeping is a moral activity, as far as it keeps one away from cafes and low places and puts before the beekeeper an example of work, order and devotion to the common cause"

—Emile Warré

7:00 AM is one of the worst hours of the day—too early if you must get up, too late if you stayed out all night. That's as far as I got before the cogs in my melon went cockeyed, and I realized I had been existing without thought on the steps of my apartment building for an unknown number of minutes. 7:00 AM was somewhere nearby, but it hadn't yet arrived because neither had Janko, a Slovene bee researcher and my mentor, who would take me to visit a queen breeder. I didn't dare sit down on the nearby bench. If I sat down, even on those cold and hard slats of wood, the day would be over before it started.

I was in Ljubljana, Slovenia. It was the first time I had lived for more than a week in an urban area, as well as my first experience in an apartment building. Being on the outskirts of the city, I could easily escape to the forests and the fields, but every day I had to come back to the concrete cage with people stomping above, vacuuming through the walls, and yelling below. At night I could sit in my bedroom window and watch on the opposite side of the courtyard six identical blocks and the flashes of life coming from each unit. A movie projection in building 4, floor 5; never-ending Christmas lights in 2/3, midnight exercise routine in 1/4. Then someone in 2/5, looking down over the courtyard, looking back at me. A mirror image in the urban reflecting pool.

How did I get here? A childhood in rural western Massachusetts. A youth chock-full of video games. A mental switch in my teens that sent me into the thrall of nature. The joy of my college years living in a cabin in the New Hampshire woods heated only by a wood stove. The burbling stream passing a few steps from the cabin, bonfires every night, playing the accordion with Max on the fiddle. My life philosophy seemingly solidified there.

After college, most of my schoolmates funneled themselves into high-powered positions in banks, consulting firms, and law schools in New York or San Francisco. I knew there were no campfires and burbling streams in those steel jungles. Instead, I took a commercial bee-keeping job in Texas, where I could live in a small town, meet colorful folk, work in nature, and not have to spend my mornings in traffic. I spent two interesting years in Texas, but then it was time for further adventure.

Slovenia snuck up on me. When applying for a research grant on honey bees (and the changing patterns of melliferous flowers over the past century), I opened an atlas and looked at the maps. Europe was next on my list, and I began to flip past pages I had heard about—England, Spain, France—into the less-familiar east—Poland, Czech, Romania ... Slovenia seemed to be a tiny and interesting hunk of geography. Not Slovakia, which is bigger and further to the north, Slovenia is tucked between Italy, Croatia, Austria, and Hungary. I knew nothing about it, nor did I have the faintest idea on how to pronounce the name of its capital, Ljubljana , but my initial research showed it was a land of small farms, beautiful countrysides, and forests. I also learned it had a long tradition of beekeeping. But what sold me on the place was an amateur YouTube video of a young fellow playing the accordion in a farm-house kitchen to an audience of six others, young and old, who were clapping along with pots and pans. I easily saw myself in that kitchen and enjoying the hell out of it.

I was awarded the scholarship and arrived in Slovenia with accordion in tow and stumbled onto something completely different. On my second day I met Luka, a Slovene painter who had just split with his girlfriend and was looking for a place to live. After a beer we decided to find an apartment together, and my world quickly tipped into Ljubljana's artistic urban scene. Instead of drinking at dive bars with old farmers, I was now following painters, poets, and philosophers to wild and strange exhibition openings, ordering rounds of schnapps until last call, and descending into grimy techno dens to meld with the thump thump thump pulse of bass until sunrise and beyond. During the day I dabbled on spreadsheets in a lab space and, slowly, the call of the forest faded. I traded my hiking boots for hip city sneakers. I hadn't been stung or smelled wax for ten months. I knew that outside the city people were playing accordions in kitchens, but my new friends kept heading into sticky-floored, smoke-filled clubs. The country mouse in the city. I lived in my block. I commuted on the bus.

The breaking day stirred with life, yet I felt hollowed out. The previous evening had progressed as many had before: starting as a few drinks with Michael and Nejc at BiKoFe. Soon, Harun joined us, then Damjan, and then Urška, who told us that something was happening at the Green Rabbit. We piled onto the cobblestones and headed across the Ljubljanica river, towards the castle brightly lit above the old town. At the Rabbit, Nitz was flipping records, the tables were full, and the feeling was warm. Then Ciniša showed up, took over the decks, and began playing amazing, twisting tracks that packed the bar's tiny alleyway with dancers. When closing hour came, Tina merely shut the door, pulled the window shades, and the drinks and music kept flowing. When I next looked at my phone it was 3 AM, and I had yet another tall absinthe cocktail in my hand. When we all finally gave up, I stepped back onto the cobblestones to find the birds chirping and the sky streaked with blue. I boarded the bus alongside some early-morning commuters, reminding me it was actually a week day. Back at my apartment, rather than dip down into an hour of sleep, I decided to make a strong cup of coffee and clean the dishes from the sink, which had been neglected for too long.

Now, at 7 AM, I gave in and sat on the cold bench. Janko would soon take me on a bee exploration across Slovenia. Normally, these were what I lived for: going to the world's small places and meeting people who were passionate about their honey bees. But today, a mere shell of a human would stand in my place. Instead of focusing on the bees, I'd be pining for sleep. Massachusetts. Texas. Hawaii. Slovenia. Is this me? Every step that brought me here made sense, but looking back at the entire journey, the arc is so strange. So, so, so strange.

17

Stung

I confess I do not like the term "anger," when applied to bees, and it almost makes me angry when I hear people speak of their being "mad," as if they were always in a towering rage, and delight in inflicting exquisite pain on everything and everybody coming near them. Bees are, on the contrary, the pleasantest, most sociable, genial and good natured little fellows one meets in all animated creation, when one understands them. Why, we can tear their beautiful comb all to bits right before their very eyes, and, without a particle of resentment, but with all the patience in the world, they will at once set to work to repair it, and that, too, without a word of remonstrance. If you pinch them, they will sting, and any body that has energy enough to take care of himself, would do as much had he the weapon.

—A. I. Root, 1882

Getting stung is part of a beekeeper's job. For some people this fact automatically filters all beekeepers into a category stamped crazy. That intelligent humans place themselves under threat from a hail of insects during their employment or hobby does seem a bit mad, but for all the fear wrapped up in the image of these flying, stinging creatures, working with bees is often not all that treacherous. Being a beekeeper requires the acceptance that there may be a flash of pain every now and again, like the way you accept your muscles will hurt when you go for a run. Once the body gets accustomed to stings, subsequent external symptoms like itching and swelling are minimal. Sometimes, when I haven't worked with bees for a while, the feeling of a sting is something I oddly miss: the small burst of life pulsing into my skin followed by antibodies rearing up to fight against the foreign substance.

On my second day in New Zealand I was finally stung, subjected to that bright spot of pain, and Keith and I were both relieved that I did not have an anaphylactic reaction. There, I learned that, opposed to wasps or yellow jackets, bees die after they sting; the barbed stinger is unable to pull out of skin, and as the bee pulls away her stomach and venom sac remains attached to the stinger, ripped from her abdomen. If you look very closely at a detached bee stinger in your skin, you can see the mechanical action of it continually pumping venom into you. This sacrifice occurs because evolution has proven that the colony is more likely to survive with a bee giving everything in one go rather than the ability to sting multiple times with less venom. It was another lesson I quickly learned: working with bees will cause some of them to die. While minimizing bee death is optimal, it is more important to treat the colony, a group of synergistically interacting organisms, as the "animal" to keep healthy and alive.

While my first stint in New Zealand taught me about being stung regularly, working in Texas led to my first harrowing experiences. The Texan bees were in a different league. A.I. Root and other scientifically-minded beekeepers would call them "defensive" because terms like "angry" and "mad" are human traits which bees are incapable of feeling. In a sober state of mind, I would label them as defensive as well. But in the thick of battle (for that was it felt like sometimes), with dozens of bees banging into my veil, digging their stingers through my leather gloves, and immediately informing me of every tiny chink in my armor, a cruder terminology rose to the surface. If a bee stung one of us in the forehead a few seconds after parking the truck thirty yards away from the hives, we would call the bees a bit "pissy". From there the names and adjectives only devolved, often including a fair number of cuss-words. It was one thing to work with bees if you could calmly open a hive and slowly look through the combs, but with four of us trying to speed through a few hundred hives in a day, calm wasn't an option. Also, we were shaking packages—slamming down the box full of comb to clear the bees from it—which is about as disrupting as someone flipping over the bed on which you were napping. It was no surprise that stingers were coming at us from every direction.

The lesson came on my first day in Texas. I knew enough to realize that sneakers were not a good idea, so I wore my hiking boots with the legs of the bee suit tucked into them. But I am tall, the boot ankles were loose, and the bee-suit was normal-sized, so after each knee-bend the legs would pull free from the boots, leaving my tender ankles exposed. Sting after sting after sting pushed through my socks. At one point a sharp reaction traveled up my body, and my scalp became so itchy I had to run fifty yards away, unclothe myself, and scratch everywhere for a full ten minutes. At that point I was wondering, as my was my boss, did I just drive from Massachusetts to Texas for a job I would have to quit after one day?

I wasn't allergic to the venom, and my apicultural dreams were not so-easily deterred, but the following morning was rough. Upon pushing myself out of bed, I collapsed on the floor, my devastated, swollen ankles unable to carry my weight. I crawled on hands and knees to the bathroom. After heaving myself onto the toilet and rolling my ankles for some minutes to get the blood flowing, and then standing with the aid of the counter, I was able to hobble into the kitchen for breakfast and get back in the yards that day. But I had learned my lesson and from then on a few layers of duct tape connected my suit-legs to boot-tops, at least until I made it to the mall for a sturdy pair of high-ankle boots.

The trauma in Texas didn't end there. Every week brought a new story with which I could entertain (or horrify) my friends and family from afar. Incidents like the first time I was stung in the face, which happened twice in twenty minutes, swelling my eye shut and distending my face flesh into a frightening resemblance of the elephant man. Or the first sting on the lip with subsequent hypertrophy which I documented by taking a picture of myself every twenty minutes as it blew up about four times in size. These face-stinging responses grew less pronounced as my body got used to the venom, but during extreme stinging incidents they would flare up. One time we arrived at a yard an hour away from the shop with a thunder storm chasing us and I realized I had forgotten my veil. I scoured the truck and eventually found a back-up veil smashed under the seat, albeit one with a golf ball-sized hole in the front mesh panel. It was not a fun afternoon. Though I tried to patch the hole with a crumpled piece of newspaper, it did little to stem the flow of bees inside the veil, who were extra defensive due to the coming thunderstorm, and stung my face without restraint. At the grocery store later that day, a mother actually turned her child out of our aisle after seeing my grotesque face and dirty appearance: an escaped circus freak perusing the tortilla chips.

After working with bees long enough, especially the Texan ones who were willing to crawl in every vulnerable crack and crevice to defend their hive, I have been stung nearly everywhere on my body. Once, when working a yard with Binford, a lifelong commercial beekeeper who was in his 80s at the time, he suddenly stood up very straight and said, "Boy! I haven't been stung there before." He took a few breaths and then bent back into the hive. I didn't have the guts to ask him where "there" was, but after a few more years of commercial beekeeping, I can say I have also been stung there, wherever it was. And yes, it hurts a lot.

If the stinging doesn't happen en masse, as in more than ten stings in a few seconds, then it's manageable. You learn to work with bees inside your suit, shirt, and pants: feeling their legs crawling on your body, wings buzzing against skin. You idly wonder if they have already stung you and are crawling around de-weaponed, until some movement of clothing presses them against your skin, and you feel that snap injection as they sting out of fear. I eventually learned how to work with bees flying inside my veil. If she doesn't sting your face immediately, then whatever defensive instinct drove her inside the veil in the first place has been lost and replaced by a desire to return to her hive. Soon she will start to crawl, adding an extra level of discomfort, but one gets used to that too. Sometimes I wouldn't have the opportunity to walk away from the hives and extract the bee, so I'd let her crawl up my neck, check, forehead, even onto my eye, and I would continue working one-eyed, hoping that this was not the place she would suddenly remember that I was the assailant and her job was to drive me away. Then, the natural route would bring her across the bridge of my nose and onto the other eye, with any sort of jostle or facial tic potentially jogging her memory. The worst moment for me, once, was when a bee, after an extensive crawl on my face, decided to explore up my nose. The tickling was too much, and I snorted, causing the bee to sting my inner nostril with head and thorax still in my nasal cavity. My immediate reaction, after a strange and gurgling yelp, was to use the veil to squeeze my nostrils, smashing the bee and unleashing a very odd scent followed by streaking nasopharyngeal pain. Ten minutes later I was still lying in the grasses yonder: a sneezing, snorting, crying, mucous-frothing mess.

Working in Hawaii was a different cup of soup. Hawaiian bees seem to take their cues from the local island spirit: just relax, man. We didn't wear coveralls, almost never used gloves, and veils were a good thing to carry in the truck, but mostly optional. I would still get stung ten, fifteen, or twenty times a day, not-infrequently in the face, but the vulnerability was worth the freedom of the sun on my skin. I couldn't bear to spend all my time in Hawaii with a layer between me and the sea breeze.

That said, Hawaii was also the place I received the most painful stings of my life. Each beekeeper will argue his or her least favorite stinging spot, but for me it is when the bee, somehow, digs her stinger into the tender flesh underneath my fingernail. This was not unusual because we spent most of the time working without gloves, rooting through piles of bees in the corner of a nuc while looking for the queen. There is a moment after the bee stings under your fingernail when it doesn't yet hurt, and you quickly dig the stinger out hoping that it won't (sometimes a bee sting doesn't hurt at all, as if she didn't inject venom, or that particular spot has already been stung and the receptors were deadened to pain), but most often the pain does come, sweeping up your arm, through your body and clouding over your head so even your vision shunts down into an epic, piercing, pulsing body scream, all stemming from an insect touching a miniscule, very sensitive part of your body. The force of it is enough to take over nearly every thought in your brain, so you are left with only the most basic of bodily functions—breathing in, breathing out, breathing in, breathing out, breathing in—until some semblance of consciousness shoves itself through that high, sustained note of pain to whisper in your ear: it will pass. It will pass. It will pass.

18

Buenos Aires Hive

2011

From the outside, today's common beehive looks like a miniaturized, windowless office building. Honey bees spill out of the long narrow entrance at the bottom, hustling to flowers and returning with stomachs filled with nectar and small balls of pollen attached to their legs. They are checked by guard bees at the landing platform before being allowed inside to deposit their load. Inside the hive is a city of activity. Crawling in the darkness over a series of vertical, evenly-spaced wax combs, the bees communicate with sound, touch, and a mix of pheromones, the last of which can send intricate messages throughout the colony in minutes. To look inside, the beekeeper must pry off the top of the hive, and the mysterious, complex world is thrust into the light. At this disturbance, the bees collectively buzz, and some may fly to defend the hive, but most ignore the intrusion and continue their activities. The beekeeper, with poise that take years to learn, as well as a diplomatic puff of smoke, is able to extract a frame from the colony to get a closer look at what is happening inside the hive.

The buzz is the first thing I notice when I walk past the security guard and step into La Rural, a convention center in Buenos Aires, Argentina. It's a mixture of many sounds—activity, lecture, network, commerce, laughter—but the reverberations inside the stadium-sized room create an ambient hum. People walk past with purposeful AM strides, their coffee cups held level while their name-badges swing and beat about their stomachs. Others are seated, weary already, leafing through the lecture summaries and trying to plan the day ahead. It's slow now, but in a few hours these passageways will fill, and the buzz will increase. Before stepping into the flow, I look up and wonder what would happen if a giant ripped off the roof of the building and sent a puff of smoke into the room. Would everyone freak out? Or would they fuss for only a moment before returning to their normal business?

This is Sunday morning at the 2011 Apimondia, the final day of a week-long international conference on honey bees. This gathering is held every two years in a different city and on different continents. Beekeepers, scientists, apitherapists, honey exporters, development workers, product vendors and bee friends gather together to celebrate the industrious and charismatic *Apis* family.

It is an interesting assemblage for those, like me, who come to learn the latest research on all the topics in bee-dom. But it is also fun to see who gathers here. Something about the bee profession attracts, or perhaps creates, odd characters. They are farmers whose livestock— thousands of stinging insects—sometimes actively try to kill their caretakers. Beekeepers can be stung dozens of times during the day yet will toss and turn at night thinking of ways to help their charges. Also, it seems like most beekeepers are happiest when alone with their bees on a sunny day. Still, an event like this brings them out of their honey houses, their laboratories, and their dirty trucks into a giant social gathering, much like the bees they care for. At these conferences I learn not only about bee science, but I get a deeper insight into the mentality of beekeepers and researchers as well.

When I step into the convention center on Sunday, I re-enter the world I had left only twelve hours earlier. At this point it seems normal to be surrounded by people who can speak extensively on honey bees. At first the feeling was overwhelming. While waiting in line to register on the opening day, I overheard two men having an animated discussion on tracheal mites. Having worked with bees for four years, I knew what they were talking about, but it dawned on me that everyone else in line understood this language as well. After being able to talk about these obscure subjects with only a select few people, I had slipped into an alternate universe where the seven thousand people surrounding me knew and feared the words *Varroa destructor*.

I open my guide book to see what lectures are on and find that I had circled "Beekeeping in the Pacific". I wander across the hall to the correct auditorium and find it nearly deserted. It's early in the day, and there are only fourteen people in the three hundred seats. On the stage a moderator sits alone behind a table, for even some of the upcoming speakers have not arrived, while the current speaker is droning on like even she wishes she were still in bed.

She is from New Zealand and is giving a presentation on Manuka—a honey highly touted for its medicinal properties. It is produced from a shrub found only in New Zealand—the honey I gulped down during my first few weeks beekeeping with Keith. Because of the limited production and the health lore associated with it, Manuka can be sold for $32 per kilo as opposed to approximately $8 for most honeys. Apparently, a lot had changed since my days beekeeping there. Finding and defending locations surrounded by Manuka had become a cutthroat affair.

On the screen at the front of the room is a photo of a helicopter flying with a pallet of four beehives hanging from a rope thirty feet beneath it. The speaker tells us it is actually cost-effective to helicopter hives into road-less, Manuka-rich areas so the bees can make this precious honey. What she doesn't tell us, and what most lay-people don't seem to understand, is that Manuka honey's proven benefits are for external wounds: burns, scrapes and other injuries. Though it has a lovely taste, people paying the large price tag are not likely to gain anything by consuming it. This fact is often politely unmentioned by Manuka vendors, as are as the rumors that there is more Manuka honey sold than produced every year.

The lecture soon lags, and I'm planning my escape when Sam and his duffel bag slide into the seat next to me. Sam is a young beekeeper and one of the few Americans here. He is the owner/operator of Anarchy Apiaries: the words "Swarm the State" cover the back of his bright green business card. While many people at the conference are dressed in suits and ties, Sam looks as if he just came from working on the farm. He wears a floppy bucket hat, scruffy beard and a sleeveless shirt that shows off two different bee tattoos. His duffel bag is with him because last evening he slept in one of the city's public parks after we had spent an hour playing music on the street, he on the ukulele and I on the jaw harp. He whispers that there is a good lecture on "Collaborative Stock Enhancement" coming up, so I gather my things, and we head out the door.

In the hall we immediately run into Victor who greets us with a big smile and a warm pat on the shoulder. There is no escaping from Victor. He is an Argentinian beekeeper who speaks no English, and Sam and I speak very little Spanish, yet one night we shared a few hours of broken conversation over pizza. We eventually understood that Victor had been awarded a free pass to the conference and took a twenty-odd hour bus ride to Buenos Aires, but his pass somehow did not allow him to attend any lectures. So he eternally roams the Expo area, and it is impossible not to run into him. We start another little chit-chat, talking about nothing once again, and Sam quickly peels off to get to the lecture. I'm less enthusiastic about stock enhancement, so Victor and I begin to wander through the booths.

The Expo fills the room. The booths are a variety of bee-related companies from around the world; queen bee breeders from Argentina, equipment manufacturers from China, and honey exporters with small, windowed conference rooms that allow the passerby to spy on the wheeling and dealing. My favorite stalls offer a line of wine glasses, each filled with a different honey. The tastes, colors, and textures of the honeys depend on what flower the bees gather the nectar from and can vary wildly. I have counted thirteen of these honey-tasting stalls in the Expo, each of which I visit two or more times a day, and I steer Victor towards one for a morning pick-me-up. I dip a wooden popsicle stick in each honey and savor the flavor—alfalfa from the US, chestnut from Italy, basswood from Ukraine, quillay from Chile. Single-source honeys have as much complexity in flavor as good wine, far from the blended, flavorless sweeteners found in generic supermarket brands. Victor starts a conversation with a fellow honey-taster, and with him distracted I slip a few of my used popsicle-sticks in his open pocket. The woman behind the counter giggles, but I put my finger over my lips and sneak away.

I find a cup of coffee and head to what promises to be an interesting lecture. Dr. Jeff Pettis, one of the leading American figures in honey bee science, is talking about Colony Collapse Disorder, also known as CCD, an issue which has brought bees and beekeeping into the news over the past eight years. CCD is a mysterious ailment. Beekeepers open their hives in the early spring and find only a queen and a handful of baby bees left in the hive. Normally these hives would be robbed of their honey, but the other bees leave the hives and honey stores mysteriously untouched.

"Declining honey bee health is complex," Pettis says, a sentence which sums up his lecture. Scientists, the press, and the general population are happiest when something like CCD or cancer or climate change can be attributed to one factor, and then they can devote themselves to finding a silver bullet that can cure the problem. In beekeeping, with stressful migratory beekeeping practices, poor nutrition, various diseases and pests, plus low-level and long-term exposure to multiple pesticides, including those that the beekeeper purposely puts in the hives, there are clearly a number of complex interactions at work. The answer is not simple.

Every now and then a scientific paper that sounds definitive will make the headlines: "Scientists at X University discover that Y is the cause for CCD." Sometimes, it is an overly-ambitious researcher publishing their findings before completing a rigorous study; sometimes the press latches onto a paper in a questionable scientific journal and runs with it or generalizes results in ways that are palatable to a gullible public that is hoping for answers. Either way, misinformation abounds.

Various pesticides, mainly the controversial neonicotinoids, are often blamed for CCD, but the science on these is still not definitive. Studies which expose bees to ten, twenty, or fifty times the dosage they would experience in the normal field setting often make the news with their dramatic findings. These headlines misinform the public while temporarily advancing the author's career, and provide fodder for the vocal individuals who wade through all of the research until they find a study—or even a fragment of a study—that supports their argument.

Neonicotinoids are used in a plethora of home and garden products that can be applied in various concentrations. These remain easy to purchase and are unlabeled as to their harmful effects to pollinators. Even with a million-signature petition calling for the ban of these pesticides, it is not likely that the powerful American Farm Lobby will give them up without some serious proof. It's true that neonicotinoids are not perfect, but are a far sight better than the deadly pyrethroids and organophosphates that were previously employed. One can only hope that this widespread attention to widespread pesticide use leads to continued development of safer farming methods.

While deaths of honey bees in the US have been high for the past seven years, averaging at around forty percent of hives, what is interesting is the average overwintering loss previously was about twenty percent. It has been normal for one-fifth of beehives to die every winter from a variety of causes, but beekeepers have been able to recover their numbers by multiplying their own hives or buying newly produced hives the following spring. The number of beehives in America is based not on ecology but on economics. Frequently, commercial beekeepers have giant cities of beehives that are kept alive not by the amount of nectar in the surrounding environment but by an artificial diet of pollen supplements and sugar syrup pumped into the hives. If the massive population of humans in Asia desires more almonds to snack on, and the almond orchards plant more trees to produce them, the growers then need more beehives for pollination, and the beekeepers will increase their numbers to fulfill their pollination contracts.

Though this recent episode of CCD has been frightening, it is important to note that there have been similar unexplainable bee disappearances in the past. No less than eighteen episodes of widespread bee death have been described internationally since the birth of industrial beekeeping in the 1860s, though probably none have had the same breadth as this most recent one. Most have lasted a few years before the bees mysteriously recovered; this latest problem seems to have dissipated as well. Even with the CCD "gloom and doom" of these past few years, the US still produced a record honey crop in 2010.

Jeff Pettis is still talking. He warns of researchers who use the phrase "in my opinion" before stating their wishy-washy conclusions, and then intentionally says the phrase "in my opinion" before concluding his lecture. He is one of the researchers in this field who is thorough and diligent in his work, the opposite of the sensationalists, and in addition to having a sense of humor, he is unafraid to admit that the experts are still searching for answers.

I take out my booklet and look at the list of lectures scheduled for the rest of the day. Merely reading some of the titles makes the air around me unbreathable: Queen Honey Bee Longevity, Aging and Royal Jelly Proteins: Have We Moved Forward?"(Slovakia); Prevalence Rate of Nosemosis in 4 Ecozones in Iran (Iran); Fungi Presence and Myco-toxins in Africanized Honeybee Hives Affected by Brazilian Sac Brood (Brazil); Characterization of Pro-Biotic Potential of *Lactobacillus* sp. Isolated from *Apis mellifera* Bee Bread for Development of Functional Food" (Colombia).

A quick calculation shows that at twenty minutes per lecture, and twenty talks per hall per day, there are around five hundred different lectures on honey bees this week. That would be five hundred different people who make their bread and butter from studying these small insects, and these are just a fraction of the world's bee scientists.

Across the room are rows of freestanding walls with posters that switch every half day, the work of hundreds of other people from around the world who devote their lives to the branches—not even branches, but the capillaries—of this corner of academia. Their work has meaning only to a highly selective group, all reaching a tiny bit further into the abyss of undiscovered knowledge about bees.

Outside the lecture hall I bump into Janko, the bee researcher I worked with at the University of Ljubljana in Slovenia. Janko looks like a failed mad scientist at the moment; under his glasses he has a burned and peeling face, and both of his hands are still wrapped like a mummy from a minor explosion in his laboratory. A few days earlier, in this same state, he gave a startling lecture on how many of the "Save the Bees" campaigns were merely bogus fronts to garner sympathy for big corporations or just plain money-making schemes. Bees are charismatic little insects, and some unscrupulous individuals and corporations have taken advantage of the public concern of bees to satisfy their mercenary ploys.

The exploitation of bees isn't Janko's only interest. This man is full of ideas and tells me about them over lunch. His latest scheme is a quasi-cheese substance made from the juices of crushed bee larvae. He just needs to perfect the recipe and find a market. "Maybe somewhere upscale," he says. "The French might find it palatable. It's protein, right? No different than milk or eggs?" I nod as I chew on my milanesa steak.

On the way back to the convention center, I bump into Alejandra, a 23-year old, bright-eyed Chilean queen breeder I had been introduced to earlier in the week. It didn't take long before her good nature and wicked sense of humor came out, and we were laughing together over picso sours. But today, her eyes hidden behind dark sunglasses, she moans that she had gone to bed at 9 AM, it now being about 1 PM. I sympathize, for I had been in this condition the day before.

On Friday night I was on my way home to have a quiet dinner when a combination of unexpected circumstances whisked me past an ambivalent guard and into the conference's VIP dinner. It was a standup, chatty affair, and though the ramped-up dress code called attention to my shorts and sandals, I was already through the gate. I couldn't stop smiling as I passed trays of finger foods and tables laden with fine Argentine beef. "How did you get in here?" people asked, and I could only shrug my shoulders, sip my wine, and smile.

After a whirlpool of mingling and a ridiculous number of group photos, the music began: first, a tango performance with a live band, then, a choreographed group dance, and, after that, a DJ-driven dance party replete with jackets swung above heads, the YMCA song (though no one knew what to do after the "Y"), and the spectacle of a guest being tossed up in the air, caught, tossed up and caught, tossed up and whoops! almost dropped, but no one hurt. Only laughter and hugs.

A Conga line formed, then dissolved, then formed again. This is how beekeepers cut loose, I kept thinking as I became a link in the chain. How many Conga lines can happen in one evening? Then it dissolved into a free-for-all kumbayah party, and I found my dance partner in a tiny Argentinian lady with long gray dreadlocks. She was probably twice my age, and I was twice her height, but we smiled and laughed and danced until the music hit its final note.

When the party crowd was turned out on the street, there was no question of stopping the festivities, and it turned into a wild night on the Buenos Aires town. Drinks flowed one way while money drained the other to the ever-pulsing beat of the music. I had no concept of time passing until I walked outside for a breath of air and saw light growing on the eastern horizon.

Only a few hours later, a little responsibility bird dragged me out of bed to attend the opening lecture at 8 AM, which was a punishing, graphic presentation on how bee propolis can be used to treat conjunctivitis and psoriasis. A enlarged photo of an infected rabbit eye made me briefly curl up in a fetal position over a few seats.

The following seminar was given by a Russian scientist on the timely topic of Apinarcotherapy, or treating alcoholism with bee stings. A quick glance around the room showed that I was not the only hungover person in the audience. The lecturer stated that alcohol is a part of culture, as well as necessary for "oxidization", and that non-drinking has negative psychological consequences. He claimed that when alcoholics are treated with bee venom, the increased desire to drink is suppressed. Though this presenter didn't seem to have any real science to back it up, my hurting head did not need much convincing.

Back to Sunday after lunch, my first step into the hall shows that the day has truly started. Tall, formally-dressed northern-European men stand next to a huddled group of poncho-clad Bolivian beekeepers who warily watch their surroundings. Four Chinese guys walk by in fuzzy yellow-and-black bee costumes. They are still dressed from a dance performance of two days ago. Business-casual is the theme, and the black and yellow color combination is common. The Mexican beekeepers look smart with their red, white and green ponchos and it is easy to pick out an Argentinian by the argyle sweater, thermos under the arm and a mug of yerba mate in hand.

Every now and then someone in traditional garb stands out of the crowd. At one booth I find a Korean lady in an ornate pink and white silk dress selling electronic and microscopical products, including one machine used for the artificial insemination of queen bees. With this gadget one can render a virgin queen unconscious with carbon monoxide and inseminate her using a tiny semen-filled syringe. I stop at the booth to chat with the lady, asking her detailed questions about artificial insemination (How fresh does the semen have to be? Can it be frozen? What temperature does it have to be warmed up to?) but she is a stone-cold professional and without a crack in her facade I make my retreat. Walking down one Expo lane I spy the ever-present Victor heading in my direction and duck into a side alley.

The afternoon lectures range from interesting to boring to impenetrably dense to inane. I walk into one auditorium to find a small, bald Indian man with a huge white mustache shouting into a microphone. He is speeding through slides of figures, charts, graphs, and pictures, barely touching on one before moving on to the next. He shows a video of some honey hunters in Yellapuor, India. "They are short, and they are very good at climbing," he says as an introduction to the video, which is then inexplicably shown at triple speed, twice. "They are very good at drinking and climbing," he says again, as a conclusion.

In the next room a German scientist is speaking English but loses me in his first sentence. Every two words are stuck between an "ahh, ahhh, ahhh," as if his ideas are too big to flow out of the pipe in his brain in one piece, so they are broken down and come out in small spurts. Another nearby lecture I pop into is entitled "N Chromosome Royal Jelly for Disease Control and Increasing Human Libido". There isn't an open seat in the auditorium, and after listening intently to the lecture I realize the speaker had not mentioned "human libido" once outside of the introduction. Lesson learned: add the words "Increasing Human Libido" to the end of any title, and people will come to your lecture.

Outside I take a seat on a bench to gather myself. Soon I feel a tap on my shoulder, and I look up to see Dorothy, an elderly, slightly-mustachioed New Zealander. I had met her the previous day when we were sitting on a similar bench, and it took her less than a minute to point out that we were both wearing bright, lime-green tee shirts. She followed her remark with a hearty laugh and a kindly arm squeeze. She was attending the conference with her daughter, who appeared to be having some of the most horrible days of her life, but Dorothy was having a "charming" time. It only took a few sentences of conversation before she pulled out a book-sized photo album to show me pictures of her "wee honey shop" just south of Christchurch on the South Island. From there, the pictures continued to her garden, her house, and, of course, her cats. I could tell the way she lingered on the cat photos that she was worried about them, that maybe they weren't getting enough food or attention while she was away.

Dorothy is looking weary as she sits next to me today. I had caught a glimpse of her sleeping through a lecture earlier. "It's a lot," I say, looking at everything, and she grabs her head and gives a moan. It has been a long week. He daughter isn't with her anymore and we are no longer wearing lime green. We basically have the same conversation we had the day before, but she is so genuine and nice that I just nod along as my eyes follow a very large man presiding over a nearby honey-tasting stand. No one is near him, and I see him glance around before dipping a wooden stick and tasting his own honey. Dorothy begins pulling out her photo album to show me her cats, but I don't want to do it again. I apologize, say there is an important lecture on collaborative stock enhancement coming up and make my escape.

There is no lecture at that moment, but there are some things I still want to do before the end of the day. I walk to one of the central booths, a tall, hexagonal affair which acts as the home base for the Apimondia Honey Queen. I had passed the booth a number of times during the week and caught glimpses of this year's queen, a beautiful young Indian woman, chatting and posing for photos. This time she is free, and I step in to say hello and ask her about her duties as the Honey Queen. Before I can get beyond a few sentences, however, I feel a sudden tension. A glance to the side shows that her parents are here as well, and the paternal stare of the short, turbaned father is so unnerving that I stumble over my remaining words, take a picture and quickly leave.

Now, there is nothing between us and the closing ceremonies. I slowly walk around the Expo one final time, taking in everything before it is dismantled, and this hall becomes an empty space. The next convention to be held in this building, which I saw advertised outside, has something to do with babies. Next week, bees will be forgotten and this hall will be filled with mothers discussing cutting-edge diaper and stroller technologies.

I return to the main hall's entrance and join the growing line. We wait there for an hour past what is supposed to be the starting time, and I meet an old Humboldt hippie beekeeper who tells me about his LSD days on tour with the Allman Brothers. Nearby things are heating up between the Chinese and Koreans—the two countries are vying to host the 2015 Apimondia. The two groups are standing a few feet apart, waving banners, flags, and yelling songs at each other. A Chinese man grabs a Korean fan and waves it in the air, yelling "China! China!" I brace for scuffle, but the doors to the hall open, and everyone pushes inside. Though I do not have a ticket to attend the closing ceremonies, I am able to sneak past officials who look overworked and confused, and I find a prime seat in the first ten rows.

After a bit more delay, the Argentinian delegation climbs on stage with the president of Apimondia wearing an official necklace that looks like a string of machine gun bullet cases hanging down to his belly. Various awards are handed out to proud recipients while the president fidgets between handshakes. Official conference photographers snap pictures of the winners for the best honey, best mead, best journal, and best beekeeping invention of the past year.

When it is the president's turn at the microphone, he gives a long speech consisting mostly of thank yous, and, at the end of it, he is merely listing names. "Carlos ... Veronica ... Sonia." His voice cracks with emotion. With every name mentioned someone climbs onstage. Hugs are freely given and "We are the Champions" by Queen is brought up on the sound system as the list of rolls on. More than fifty people are crowded around the podium, and now the volunteers wearing purple shirts are called up.

The people on stage are acting as if they are in some sort of rock band, waving and trying to pump up the crowd, but the audience gave its initial wave of applause minutes ago and is not willing to reciprocate any energy. The Queen song finishes but then plays a second time with more onstage waving, hugs, tears. Alejandra the Chilean is sitting next to me and whispers, "The Argentinians are exaggerators. Everything they do has to be the best. The best wine. The best beef. The most beautiful women. The best Apimondia. Bah!" She gives dismissive wave of her hand. I look up and see the turbaned father of the Apimondia Queen on the stage. He has been pushed by the growing crowd, so he is standing next to my gray-dreadlocked Argentinian dance partner. The president comes to the end of the list, "We are the Champions" reaches its peak, and, finally, the audience, sensing the end, gives a decent cheer. In what looks almost like an afterthought, turbaned father throws his arm around gray-dreadlocks, and together they both take a bow.

I stand up and start to applaud.

When I get back to the hostel that night, it's late, and I am exhausted. I want nothing more than to sleep for the next twelve hours, and, though it feels odd to say, I am ready to stop talking, thinking, and breathing honey bees. It is time for a break.

The final portion of the closing ceremony was intense. Before the delegate's vote on who would be the next Apimondia host, the Chinese team filed a complaint, claiming the Koreans violated a rule in their promotional presentation. One Chinese delegate jumped on stage and in an impromptu, impassioned and impractical speech promised free hotel rooms and plane tickets to everyone if China hosted the next Apimondia. He wouldn't stop talking until the microphone was physically taken away from her. Perhaps this incident was the tipping point, and when the tally came in a few minutes later, South Korea won by twelve votes.

In my hostel room, I squeeze a dollop of toothpaste on my brush and head towards the bathroom. In the common area I find a group of Colombian beekeepers sitting around a table and drinking beer. We had bumped into each other in the mornings over breakfast, at the Expo during the day, and I had heard their snores during the night. They are still talking about beekeeping, and as I walk by they motion for me to sit down, sliding an extra beer to an empty seat. "It's our last night," one says. "We won't meet for another two years."

"Two years?" I reply, thinking of all the days that I will spend outside of this hive between now and then. "Okay," I hear myself say. "Maybe one more ..."

19

Chile Awake

2012

I wake up on the floor of an outside balcony, five stories off the ground, with my head next to a dozen or so small, potted cacti. Turning, I look through the sliding glass door and see feet, only feet, crossing the floor of the living room. I know it's time to get up but I flip over anyway, my hip pressing through the air mattress to the hard tile, to relish a few more minutes of sleeping-bag warmth.

In the other direction, through the metal bars of the railing, I look down on Renaca, Chile, shrouded in the early morning fog. I can see a lawn and small pool directly below me but the hillside, beach and ocean are currently hidden in a cloudy white paste.

It is Monday morning. Francisco and I had stayed the weekend at the apartment of his girlfriend, Kenka, and we have woken up early to get back to Limache, forty minutes inland, to start a week of beekeeping. Francisco is my boss, but also more: some combination of friend and adopted father. A month earlier I had come to the Apimondia in Argentina on a one-way ticket, with little plan for after but having some idea that I wanted to work in South America for a season. At the conference I had met Alejandra, Francisco's daughter and beekeeping partner, and after only knowing me for a few days, they invited me across the Andes. We lived, ate, worked and often spent the weekends together, and it didn't take long until I felt part of the family—a long lost cousin, whose Spanish needed a good drag out of the gutter before he could catch every drop of the torrent gushing around the dinner table.

I spent my days feeding bee colonies, grafting larvae, catching queens, putting queen cells in nucs, picking up equipment, moving wood, evaluating hives, moving brood into cell builders, replacing queens—the standard queen-breeding work. Some mornings it was scraping the insides of boxes: just plain old manual labor. In my low moments, my mind would drift back to a half-year earlier when I had a prestigious scholarship to do research in Europe, and then juxtaposing that with the present: a semi-illegal foreign worker doing grunt work for a fraction of an American salary. But most times I would remind myself that almost everyone in the world thinks they are underpaid and underappreciated. I was in Chile, in the sunshine, practicing my Spanish, and there was a box of amazing, ripe avocados waiting for me at the end of the day. Plus, I was in my ideal line of work: beekeeping in an exotic location. "Have hive tool, will travel" had been my motto for the past five years. Under the light of introspection, the bothersome thoughts would dissipate and the mornings would fly by as I worked alongside the other men, Odwaldo humming away in the hive next to me, interjecting oddities every now and then. "Paharitos!" he sings out, and tosses another box on top of the already teetering tower of woodwork.

The morning is done at noon sharp. When the hour strikes, we close the hives, brush off the dust and walk back to the burnt-orange-and-green house under a sunlight that had just started to make itself known. Carmencita, a tiny Chilean woman whose head doesn't reach my sternum, is finishing up lunch in the kitchen and when she sees me her face crinkle up into a giant smile. She puts the final touch on the cazuela, a Chilean chicken soup, and we dish it out into sturdy brown bowls.

Before I take my first bite I gently remind myself of all the smashed sandwiches and ugly plastic Tupperware I have previously lunched from—most of my lunch breaks consisted of swallowing a few bites in the car while driving between yards. But in Chile lunch is the cornerstone of the day: a pleasant, home-cooked meal with Francisco and his two daughters Rocio and Alejandra. They speak in Chilean—a slang-filled deformed version of Spanish that flows so fast it took my ears months to adjust. I listen for a bit, then drift away until Francisco interjects, "You see, sir Williams? You see?" and I say si, si, as if I had been paying attention all along. Francisco eats a bowl of soup with his chin extended over the table, rapid scoops into his mouth, and sometimes his two daughters would make fun of him for that, his clothes, the way he sneezes, and so on. Sometimes I defend him, sometimes I join their side.

Sometimes lunch turns into a serious discussion, one I can only understand the fringes of, and I eat silently as they argue over business, family and other issues. We lived together in tight quarters, I in a room separated from the hallway by only a curtain, and the kitchen is a constant traffic jam, our meals peppered by requests to pass the salt, the oil or the sugar-drops for the tea.

With soup bowls empty we all take a cup of green tea, and I move outside to the hammock for the remainder of the lunch hour. Freddy, the family dog, sticks his muzzle over the hammock's side for a few minutes of pets until he settles down for his own siesta. The droning traffic from the road below and the sweet green tea swirl my thoughts until I am somewhere in-between sleeping and waking for the next half hour until I hear the slap of the door frame and I break out of the drowse refreshed, thankful, and ready to tip over into the rest of the day.

On some afternoons, we drive to an avocado orchard an hour away where Francisco keeps over a thousand hives. The orchard takes up an entire valley: avocados planted on the steep, upper hillsides, citrus trees below, and fat red table grapes on the valley flats. Black rubber irrigation hoses snake up the hillsides, watering each tree, but the irrigation stops abruptly, in a straight line across the mountain, above which is desert where even the scrub brush seems to have a difficult life. Roads break up the avocado jungle and groups of 30 or so hives lay every few hundred meters. We slowly make our way through the yards around a ring road at one altitude, then a steep road takes us to the next and we work back around the valley just fifty meters higher.

These colonies are here for pollination purposes: without them there would be no avocados. The orchard served a purpose for Francisco as well: protection. Nothing is safe from thieves in Chile, especially beehives. The stories I heard were both hilarious and disconcerting; Francisco once woke up to find the truck in his driveway on blocks, all the wheels had been stolen during the night. Another time, after years of getting out of his truck to open the gate of his property, he installed an automatic gate-opener. Four days later, the automatic arm was stolen. Beehives, which are often in farmland and away from houses, are notoriously in danger, even behind a locked gate. But the orchard provided protection: an electric fence surrounding the entire valley, with seven armed guards patrolling at night. Even avocado theft can prove profitable in this country.

The orchard manager knows the game as well; he needs the bees as much as they need him. The price per hive in the contract, if there is one, will change depending on the success of the season. I sit in the truck watching Francisco speak with the manager in front of the office, check in hand. After sealing the deal with a handshake, he returns to the truck.

"Not as much as it is supposed to be," he tells me, "but it's something."

When we get back to Limache, even after a ten-hour day, Francisco quickly changes into shorts, t-shirt and a floppy hat, and hits the hills. He is a man of extremes—some of his personal stages were characterized by a proliferation of drink and smoke, but when I arrived he was a recent teetotaler with a new favorite hobby of running. He still often described beekeepers he knew as "good beekeeper, smokes very good weed" and even had a secret stash of "really good stuff" which in desperate times Alejandra had searched high and low for, but the hiding place remained a mystery.

At around 9 PM, with Francisco freshly showered and wearing a Pink Floyd t-shirt, suspenders and jeans, we gather back at the kitchen table for a small dinner of leftovers or "avocado smash" on toast. If it is just two of us, Francisco gradually slips into a monologue, telling me his plans for the bee business, his dreams, his troubles, and I nod along, offering a word of support or advice every now and then. "This is the point," he interjects every now and then, or "I think it's a good idea," and I agree or disagree as I see fit.

While talking, he gathers the spilt crumbs into a small pile with his finger, pushed one way, then other: a small, crumby pyramid. If a block of cheese is on the table, around once a minute one of us slices off a tiny piece to eat, and this steadily continues until the cheese is gone. "Thank you very much, Sir Williams," he says to me when I hand him the thermos of hot water that I know he wants, but is too distracted by his story to interrupt himself.

This routine and day ahead rolls through my early-morning mind on that balcony in Renaca until Francisco appears with a tall glass of murky liquid. "Banana milk," he says. I sit up and we clink glasses before drinking deeply. Next he brings me a shot of yerba mate—a highly caffeinated tea—and with a few sips of that sleep is forgotten. After saying goodbye to Kenka, we are out the door. Francisco presses the elevator button and the machine wakes up.

"You see," he says to me with a smile, "this is my life."

I want to say thanks—thanks for showing it to me and sharing your knowledge. Thanks for being so welcoming and kind to a stranger. Thanks for fulfilling my dreams of living and working with bees in South America, introducing me to new tastes, smells and experiences, for making me laugh, and filing my head with ideas that I would not have gotten if I had stayed at home. I want to say all of these things, but it's too early for such a speech, and I mumble something else to fill the space. The elevator doors open, and we both step in, the week rising to meet us.

20

Chile Queen

2012

⚕

"Wow!"

Francisco's high-pitched exclamation popped across the bee yard. Late afternoon sun slanted between us. Francisco didn't continue his thought and we were left with the steady symphony of insect wings and the occasional engine echo from the road at the base of the hill. I looked at the hive spread open before me. Seven frames covered in bees leaned against the wooden base. A better practice is to add space in the hive by removing only two frames and then shifting the other seven around the box like files in a file cabinet, keeping most of the bees inside. But I couldn't find this hive's queen, and I was feeling desperate. She was failing, and I needed to replace her.

The bees seemed to continue their normal tasks even as a giant creature handled their domicile like a stack of lumber. Why don't they care? I asked myself. How had we bred these insects to be so docile and not attack the intruder in full force? A few guard bees buzzed my head, but after another puff, they all went back to in-hive business. Looking at the seething mass of insects, I realized that if even a fraction of this hive decided to turn their stingers on me, I'd be helpless. It was a good thing I liked the *Where's Waldo* books as a kid, because a big part of being a beekeeper is trying to find one slightly bigger bee in a box of 20,000.

"These are good bees," Francisco mulled aloud. He was working on another row of hives across the dirt track behind me. We were on the upper part of his property, behind the grafting house, in a mid-summer inspection. The other part of the crew was catching queens on the final section of the loop that meandered up the hillside. I took out one of the side frames of my open hive and held it up to the light. There was a minimal chance that the queen was on the side frames—she usually hangs out in the center of the nest with the eggs and larvae, while side frames are used for honey storage—but if I had applied too much smoke, she might have scurried into a corner. I didn't find her on the first side frame, or the second, and then the box was empty of frames but full of bees running hither and thither on the wooden walls and mesh floor. I bent over and stuck my head into the open hive to get a closer look.

Positioning myself so not to block the light, I reached around my bulky veil and poked at a pile of bees in the corner, searching for any sign of that enlarged abdomen. The vast hum of the bees in the open air transformed into the buzzing echo inside the wooden walls. I closed my eyes, breathed in the hive's air, and imagined what it would be like to exist in this space. Life would be all darkness, buzzing, and pheromones until that glorious moment of leaping from the hive's entrance into the blazing, colored world. When I opened my eyes, I spotted her crawling up the side of the box. Standing up, I plucked the queen from the wood, whispered a small appreciation, then crunched her between my fingertips.

"These are bad bees," Francisco groaned. While my head was in the box, he had closed one hive and moved onto the next. An amazing fact to witness—obvious only when you hear about it—was how each hive had a different personality. One hive could be diligent and productive while the one next to it could be lazy. Another hive might not ever lift a stinger while its neighbor will attack you if you walk within ten yards of it. Every hive was its own being.

Taking it even further, there are even cohorts within each hive. A queen mates with more than a dozen different drones at the beginning of her life. The semen she receives is stored in her abdomen in order of mating. The first flush of workers will all be sisters, but when that seed runs out, the next batch will be from a different father—only half-sisters to the first. If the father is from a different hive, they can have much different characteristics and the personality of the entire hive can change as one cohort is replaced. One interesting aspect about this succession is that during the process of supersedure (replacing the queen) it has been shown that the bees of each cohort will try to raise an egg from their shared father, rather than one from one of their step-dads. How in the world do they know that?

I walked the fifty yards to the grafting shack, my feet hitting the dusty ground at a slow pace, no rush to finish the day. Under the shaded canopy I opened the hive of bees where we stored the new queens and took out a cage. This queen had hatched a week ago, mated in the skies above us, caught by someone in the crew, and then stored for just this moment—to start her life as the head of a colony. I walked back to the hive with the same gait, letting my weary limbs carry me without any thought at all.

Back at the hive I put the cage on the wooden corner and began to put the frames back into the box. A clump of bees had climbed off the comb and hung like a fat, living icicle off the wood beam. Using the hive tool, I scraped the clump into my naked hand and dropped it into the hive. A new queen cannot be introduced directly into a colony because the bees would kill her as an intruder. Instead, she must be put in a matchbox-sized cage made of wood and mesh with the entrance blocked by candy—a hardened sugar paste. By the time it takes the bees to eat through the candy—a few days—they will realize that: A. their old queen is no longer around and B. this new queen and her intoxicating pheromones isn't that bad. When she is finally set free, the bees usually accept her as their new mother and she begins her life duty: laying eggs from morning until night.

With the queen cage stuck between the two center combs, I put the hive back together: the excluder, super and lid. Looking down the row, I counted four more hives that stood between me and the end of the day.

"I love my bees," I heard Francisco say behind me. I wasn't sure if he was talking to me or himself. It didn't matter.

21

Brazil Butterfly

2012

It took Celia three days before she couldn't stand it anymore. For three days I had walked in and out of her *pousada*—guesthouse—and merely said, "*Oi*," which in Brazilian Portuguese means, "Hi." It was one of the few words I knew. The week before I had been in São Paulo and quickly realized that my spoken Spanish was essentially worthless. Understanding written Portuguese wasn't too difficult with a Spanish eye, but when a word transformed into sounds it seemed to maintain only vague vestiges of its written self. For example, the English word for restaurant turns into *restaurante* in Spanish and is pronounced essentially the same as in English but with an "eh" at the end: restaurant-eh. In Portuguese it is written the same as in Spanish, but the "r" is pronounced as a sort of "hr", and the "te" is pronounced as a "ch", bringing the pronunciation to something like, "hess-to-roch." It took me several days and a few confused looks before I nailed down "hess-to-roch", but many other sound-switching syllables merely bounced again and again off my tiny, rubber brain. I would say a word about seven times with no understanding from the listener, and would have to revert back to the ever useful and nearly universal traveler communication tools: pointing and thumbs up.

Celia's pousada was in Juazeiro do Norte, a smallish city in northeastern Brazil. I had traveled there to learn about organic honey production. After completing my working stint in Chile, I began to wander

South America with half of my mind looking to find things to write about for the *American Bee Journal,* and the other half looking for adventure, beauty and delicious food. The latter had mostly elbowed out the former, but when I pointed towards Brazil—which required a three day journey on bus and train—I knew that I was heading into an important country for the global organic honey trade.

Producing certified organic honey is tricky. Not only does the beekeeper have to use organically-approved treatments for his bees (treatments which are more difficult and time-consuming compared to the synthetic options), but the bees also cannot be within a three-mile range of any conventional agriculture. If you took a map of the US and put a three-mile buffer around every bit of non-organic farm field and also removed places like national parks and wilderness areas which do not admit beekeepers, what's left are a few small slivers of land, most of which are inaccessible or unproductive.

Northern Brazil has a hot, dry climate which creates an ecosystem called *sertão*: a sort of arid, scrub-jungle where almost no commercial agriculture is possible. But whenever it rains, the scrub's flowers burst open, and honey bees enter a harvesting craze. Add to this scenario good genetics: the honey bees in Brazil are a hybrid of African and European subspecies that are naturally more resistant to the dreaded varroa mite that decimates bees in North America and Europe. Thus, when purchasing a bottle of certified organic honey (not "all natural", "bio", "ecologically friendly", or any of the other label-names that try to steer your brain into thinking "organic"), it is highly likely that the honey will be from Brazil. Let me point out that I don't believe certified organic honey is any better than honey produced "organically" (meaning without synthetic chemicals) by your local beekeeper, especially because of the significant distance this organic honey must travel to reach your shelf. But organic is a hot term in this era, one that bumps up the price tag and for some makes it worthwhile to go through the bureaucracy to get that prominent but often fallacious seal.

In the weeks before I arrived in Brazil, I asked friends and acquaintances if they had any organic honey contacts in the country. I sent inquiries to the contacts, who were mainly honey packers or beekeepers but received very few answers. Faced with just a few weeks before I would have to fly home and no strong leads to learn about organic honey, I saw two paths forward. I could go the touristy beaches for a beautiful if vacuous time and squander lots of money I didn't have, or I could go to the sertão without invitation and see what I could learn. Weighing these options, the answer that eventually came was consistent with the gut-feeling that had been steadily growing during my years of travel: the tourist-beach option gave way to a rising call for the less-known, the strange, the unbeautiful. The next day I bought a plane ticket to Juazeiro do Norte, the main city in the sertão region, and then I started researching what to do when I got there.

The flight from São Paulo to Juazeiro do Norte left at midnight and landed around 3 AM. For someone like me who didn't know the city, had no way of reserving a non-five-star hotel, and didn't speak a lick of the language, the timing was unpleasant. I disembarked the plane and pushed through the throng of sleepy, waiting families hoping I could find a taxi driver who looked decent and would understand I wanted to find affordable shelter. I soon ended up in the center of town on dead-empty streets, knocking on an iron door long enough to wake the owner, Celia.

The next morning, or I guess it was around 1 PM when I finally dragged myself out of bed, I found Celia sitting in a rocking chair in the common room. Celia looked like a former beauty queen pushing fifty, with highly-coiffed blond hair, silver amalgam shining in her smile, and a fashion sense to say she hadn't lost an inch in the game. Her red and white polka-dot high heels dramatically complemented her poofy and completely-unnecessary-due-to-the-heat shoulder jacket. We introduced ourselves, but after that we reached an impasse. Our lack of language dissolved into laughter. I shrugged my shoulders. "Não entendo" (I don't understand) was my fallback phrase, or even "Não entendo nada" (I don't understand nothing). But Celia didn't care. She began talking, her speech flowing rapidly. I could understand only fragments: like looking for a certain color in a stream of M&Ms, every now and then I saw one I recognized, but it would quickly pass beneath an avalanche of other words.

Juazeiro do Norte is a strange little city of maybe 300,000 people. It is mostly known for a priest named Padre Cicero, who is enshrined in a giant statue on the peak of a nearby hill, as well as the annual pilgrimage he inspires. Every October, some 500,000 people descend on the area to pay homage to the man. This explained why the city was littered with cheap pousadas that were currently empty, including mine. I was staying in a six-bunk room with a bathroom all to myself for around $7 a night. The small museum on the hill next to Cicero's statue held thousands of carved, wooden body parts: feet, hands, legs and even breasts hung each in their own anatomical sections along the museum's walls. The belief was that a hand-delivered wooden carving to the father would bring healing to that part of the body.

After drinking an early afternoon coffee, I found an internet café to check for responses to my requests for information about organic honey production in the area and then sent out a few more emails. I was hoping that I could wrap up an interview and beekeeper visit in a few days and then spend the remaining two weeks traveling, perhaps to the city of Fortaleza or to the northern coast. With my emails sent I

129

spent the rest of the day exploring the town, admiring the craftwork of some wooden body parts, trying a variety of fried food-balls, drinking untranslatable juices, and watching a local football match on the town's pitch. I waited an entire day before heading into the internet café again. Other than an email from my university requesting donations and my mother checking in on me, my inbox was empty.

On my third day in Juazeiro do Norte I came in from my evening walk to find Celia and Francisco, a stocky, wispy-haired fellow who did all the chores of the pousada, watching TV in the common room. They both wore jackets and looked cold, but I was comfortable in shorts and a t-shirt. I said "Oi," as was my custom, but instead of replying with the same, Celia pushed herself out of her rocking chair, walked towards me and unleashed a flurry of Portuguese. I couldn't decipher any of it, but upon hearing her serious tone I briefly entertained the possibility that I was getting kicked out of the pousada. Then Celia said something that cut through the fog: "No oi!" she admonished, her hand like a knife hitting her open palm: "Bom dia, boa tarde, boa noite!" The light went on in my brain. She wanted a true greeting: good day, good afternoon, good night.

"Si, si, entendo," I replied. "Boa noite." But Celia wasn't finished. The verbal hurricane kept coming. "Historia," she said multiple times. She was asking about my history. My country, where I was from. "Massachusetts," I said and saw them both make the same sneering face, noses up, which I had no idea how to interpret. Did they know the place? Not like it? Was it just a funny word?

The questions continued. "Where are you going? How long have you been away? Why are you here?" These were my rough translations and I answered in Spanish, unsure if it was getting through. "Mãe?" she asked, which earlier that day I learned meant mother.

"Si," I answered with a thumbs up.

"Father? Sister? Brother?"

"Si, si, no." We even got to the basics of what I did and why I was there. I knew the word for bee, beekeeper, and honey, but anything further than that was hopeless. After my crude answers were understood, Celia seemed satisfied and sat down in her chair. "Boa noite," I said and crept into my room. We were getting somewhere.

"Café!"

Francisco yelled this through the wall, which I could plainly hear, when coffee was ready in the morning. Or I should say, he yelled this when he was ready to take away and clean the coffee thermos, and I had to get out of bed. First I turned off the fan, which was my only form of protection from the overnight mosquitoes (mosquitoes, they assured me, which did not have diseases like malaria or dengue), then took a mug and a muffin from the common room and climbed back in bed, sipping the hyper-sweet coffee and reading my book. When the mug bottomed out and I tired of reading, I showered, dressed myself, and put another nail into this developing routine. Then I sat at the desk that I had co-opted from the common room and thought about what I could do to push forward the day.

Two days prior, without any reply from the honey packers, I moved onto the next stage of my plan—knocking on doors and asking questions. I had taken a bus from Juazeiro to a neighboring small town, and from there I boarded another bus that took me into the hills. It was difficult to explain to the driver where I wanted to go, but I had an address written down, and he let me off in front of a squat, L-shaped concrete building tucked into the woods. Armed with my notepad, I pounded on the most official-looking door I could find, but the only person around was a cleaning lady who, through broken conversation, told me the man I was looking for wasn't there.

The next day I tried another company, which required a bus trip in a different direction followed by a twenty-minute walk under the hot sun. Though it was supposed to be winter, the sun cruelly pecked at my head and neck. Eventually I came to a complex on a hill and knocked on an office door. A worker let me in, and we had a confusing exchange until one of them made a phone call. I spoke with someone in English—a boss. When I explained my purpose, she was very friendly and said they would email me in a day or two to arrange a visit and tour of the area. Success! I thought, closing the office door behind me. The nagging, lost feeling that had been gathering inside me loosened a bit, and I felt rather buoyant walking back to the bus stop, the sun not seeming so hot anymore. Perhaps this journey might not be a waste after all.

A dramatic telenovela played loudly on the TV in the common room, but Celia talked over it. I sat in one of the chairs while she walked around pointing and announcing the Portuguese word for different items which I repeated after her: *cadeira* (chair), *cupo* (cup), *luz* (light), *chão* (floor), *mesa* (table), and so on. She was still wearing high heels—different ones—that coordinated with her outfit. After a week here, there was only one time I didn't see her in heels. Sometimes her outfit changed in the middle of the day, and of course the heels changed with it. As my backpack held only two pairs of shorts and four shirts, I am sure she noticed the exact same details in me but through the opposite lens. Once Celia had named everything in the room, she moved back to the chair and pointed at it, looking at me, waiting for my answer. "Chãda?" I tried. "Cadeira," she said, then she pointed at the floor. I couldn't remember a wisp. "Borboleta?" I asked, throwing out my favorite Portuguese word, meaning, "butterfly."

"Ah!" she gasped, throwing her hands up in the air, and I laughed.

Soon she gave up, and I retreated to my room for a dinner of tiny, delicious bananas. It had been three days since my trip to the honey packer, and I hadn't received an email. I had emailed again and tried calling, but I reached someone who didn't speak English. After an awkward conversation, the line cut off (or they hung up on me?). Talking on the phone in a different language is more difficult than in person. Perhaps I would get an email tomorrow, I thought, and peeled another banana.

Alone on the bench, I surveyed the town's park for the hundredth time. The afternoon was spent, and night crept in to fill its place, as it did every day, whether I was there or not. A man with a music cart—a metal frame on wheels with a giant stereo system bolted to it—had just set himself up a stone's throw away from me and started blaring the same Peruvian pipe-band cover CD that he played and flogged every night of the week, with the main offender in my book being the horrendous rendition of, "My Heart Will Go On." This version is on the short list of effective songs to be used for my torture and eventual confession of secrets.

Across the way another man was setting up a trampoline. Soon this park would be filled with children and their parents. They could ride coin-driven mechanical ponies, buy balloons and neon-lit sticks, or rent kid-sized electronic toy cars and drive them as fast as possible until crashing into each other. It actually looked like a really fun place to be a kid.

I was delaying my highlight of the day, the moment of pleasure after which the day would be stamped and filed under the heading: absentia. I could see the churros cart across the square and the small cluster of kids and adults waiting for their treasure: a cylindrical piece of fried bread filled with dulce de leche. It was knee-bucklingly good. Each place I have visited in the world has at least one kind of food, fruit or meal that it does extremely well and cannot be wholly replicated elsewhere—whether it is due to atmosphere, methodology, or ingredients, I'm not sure. There were a few of these apogees I had identified in Brazil, the Sunday feijoada feast being one, but churros were my favorite and it was always my traveling prerogative to take advantage of the good and unique while I was in town.

After the churro I would find a café with a football game and a beer, or I would go back to my room and write something. Writing was a decent pastime when in limbo like this, but in these past two weeks when I read what I had produced at night in the light of morning, I only saw garbage. I still hadn't heard anything from the honey packer—the suspicious side of me said: hey, these 'organic' people might be trying to hide something. But it was more likely that they just didn't care about me writing a bee journal article on them, didn't want to be bothered, and that was that. It was something I had to accept. But I was still here, at Juazeiro central park on a Friday night, not quite willing to give up and simply travel for my final week in the country, but not able to take any more steps towards the goal. Nothing. A growing sadness in the pit of my stomach. Who cares about organic honey? No one cares. If an article did come out, would anyone read it with more than a passing interest? Would it be worth all the time I dawdled in this unknown, lackluster, mid-sized city in the north of Brazil?

133

At the nearby music cart, the next song blared, but it was not yet, "My Heart Will Go On." I could wait a few more songs before dashing for my churro. Suddenly it struck me: the book I had been reading every morning during my coffee hour was *Don Quixote*, a story about an idealist chasing his mad dream. An absurdly perfect choice. What a fool I was. I started laughing.

I had hardly closed the door to my room when there was a knock, and Celia entered. Though the room was fairly big, the bunk beds made for awkward spacing, and with Celia inside, the quarters felt close. She began talking to me, rapidly as always. "Não entendo," I said, but she was insistent and repeated herself while using lots of hand gestures: an important part of Brazilian communication, a parallel dialogue that I knew little about other than the thumbs up. As Celia talked to me her hands were going wild, including a finger waggle, brushing the backs of her hands, and bouncing her two extended pointer fingers against each other.

"Gays," she said in English. "Comprede gays, si? Dos hombres ..." She bounced her two fingers together. Was she asking me if I was gay? Or telling me I can't bring any other men here? Or ... what? I couldn't tell. But she kept repeating her words, trying to explain something to me, and I kept waiting for her to leave me alone. "Não entendo nada," I said over and over until, exasperated, she put her hands on her hips and parroted, "Não entendo, Não entendo." I put my head on the bed frame and laughed.

Finally, she did leave, but she came back a few minutes later with a pencil and a piece of paper. Then she made a rather explicit drawing, which made me laugh again, and started a twisted game of Pictionary for practically every word she wanted to get across. Finally, my bulb lit. This pousada, in the fifty-one weeks of the year when it wasn't a pilgrim's destination, was a part-time gay flophouse. The guys who came here wanted privacy, so at the right signal, which we agreed to be the word, "Borboleta," I should hide in my room.

"Entendo," I said, thumbs up. As strange as it was, the success of communication under fire made us both feel pretty good. The bottom line was that the local men-folk needed a place to hide out, and Celia needed money during the off season. Okay by me.

She left my room and I laid down. I only had a few days left anyway. It was time to call this trip a failure and move on.

Celia and I went into town together. Earlier in the afternoon I mentioned a headache, and she insisted that I get something for it, and that she would help me. There were a million pharmacies in this city, really, it seemed like one covered every corner, but Celia made me and my headache walk fifteen minutes across town in the sun to a particular one. She spoke with the pharmacist who gave me a paper bag with a few pills, and I swallowed one directly in the store. Afterwards I discovered the real reason for the journey. This pharmacy was down the street from a shoe store which catered exactly to Celia's taste. Of course, we had to stop inside for a browse.

Inside the store we ran into a girl I had met on a bus a few days earlier. We said hi again as Celia moved towards the shoes. When the girl left I remembered an interaction from the previous day when the owner of a restaurant asked me where I had been (I hadn't eaten lunch there for two days in a row). My gosh, I thought, I'm starting to get known here. I joined Celia looking at the wall of shoes.

"How many shoes do you have?" I asked in Spanish.

"Muitos," (a lot) she replied, picking up a particularly pointy purple heel.

"One for every day of the year?" She didn't answer me.

"You don't know the number?"

"No, I do."

After some deliberation, Celia bought the purple heels. She walked back to the pousada with a smile on her face. By the time we got back, my headache was getting better.

Packing and unpacking my sizable backpack was a big part of traveling life. Wrinkled clothing was the norm, and every session was a lesson in efficiency and expedience. Frequently-used goods went in the top pouch, while other clothing and items went in the large partition, layered from the bottom to the top in order of usage. Important and expensive things went in the small backpack, which never left my side. Though I had it down to a science, I felt out of practice. It had been three weeks since I had unpacked. Also, in a normal hostel, one only had the bed and a tiny locker to use, while the rest of the room was shared with other bodies and their things. Here my stuff had luxuriously spread around the six-bunk room.

I didn't mind packing now, for I was full of lightness. Two days before my plane ticket back to São Paulo, I said "screw it" and went to the honey packer one last time. They seemed a bit surprised when I walked in the door, saying they hadn't heard from me, something was wrong with their server, foreign emails weren't arriving, and a few other excuses that didn't completely hold water. They told me to return the following day. I got a full tour of the packing plant, which was actually quite impressive in its efficiency, technology, and cleanliness, as well as a ride across the county to see a beekeeper in action, followed by a long interview with the owner on Skype. I had enough information to write a series of articles, which would pay for my trip here as well as for the rest of my travels in South America.

Again, the plane left at a horrible hour, 3 AM, but Francisco agreed to drive me to the airport. Celia had said goodbye to me at a decent hour while wearing her new purple shoes. It was a funny one—my three-week friend who I couldn't really communicate with, but strangely felt a little bonded to through her kindness and curiosity. At my base I am a happy loner, but when friendly people enter my orbit, I end up enjoying them. She showed me that, despite the strange patch of aimlessness I'd found myself in, there was a bit of magic in Brazil which, with its churros, its feijoada, its fruit juices, its football, and the friendly, forward people, had slowly infected me.

Weirdly, I thought to myself watching the lit statue of Padre Cicero on the hill, I might miss this place.

22

Japan WOW

2012

Ten pummeling hours at thirty thousand feet. Multiple rounds of plane food sitting oddly in the stomach. Extremely tired but unable to sleep. Unsure of the time of day, or the day of the week. Legs stiff, neck sore and spine contorted. A few too many bad movies, small bottles of wine, and cups of coffee scraping through the veins. Stained clothing and aged sweat. These are not uncommon sensations for an American arriving in Japan.

Stopping at the first information desk I saw, I asked a pair of advertisement-perfect ladies wearing matching uniforms: "Hello, do you speak English? How do I say hello in Japanese?"

"Konichiwa," they tittered.

"And thank you?"

"Arigato." The sounds strange to my ears, I wrote these down in my notebook. These are two simple but important things to learn when entering a foreign country. One can spend an entire life learning a language and a culture, but if you get these two down, it is a tiny foot in the door, a fig leaf of effort, to start the bridge between you and the other. I could have done this research before, but as usual it got bumped off the back-end of a midnight hour packing job. Plus, there's no substitute for hearing the words in person, in place, to get the ball rolling.

Why was I in Japan? I had found a beekeeping job in Australia and the cheapest flight to Sydney took me through Tokyo. Why not stop off for a week? Plus, when I was around 10 years old, my family hosted a Japanese man for a month. His name was Manabu, and he stayed with us while he taught classes about Japan and origami in my elementary school. We stayed in contact over the years, and this seemed like a perfect time to visit him, see Japan, and, while I was here, try to learn something about Japanese beekeeping.

With legs once again moving, my blood began to circulate, and my brain began to function. First observation: everyone was tiny. At 6'5" I was used to being the long straw, but here I was by far the tallest person in sight. I followed the herd of people and pictures signaling the train terminal. At every junction I searched for more drawings, or English characters, to point me in the right direction. In my travel notebook, page 1, I had written precise instructions to my hotel. Once I was there, with a shower and little rest, I could tackle this city. This megacity. At the terminal, I tried to read the subway map, which was a massive plate of psychedelic spaghetti, and the ill feeling regained ground.

The bullet train sent the outside world into fast-forward, so I turned my attention to the compartment around me. The reserved seats had universal pictographs: a pregnant woman with lightning bolts highlighting her belly, and an old man with a cane and beard. But the letters broke my brain. No longer simple Roman lines and curves, every symbol was a cross-hatched mash-up, each an entire story in itself. I stared at instructions printed next to my seat, which were in three different languages. By the end of the train journey I deduced that Korean looked like small alien cartoons, Chinese was wilder and more complicated, while Japanese had letters very precisely cut with a samurai sword. All were beautiful, in a way, but all were also gibberish to me.

A train conductor entered, bowed, and addressed everyone in the car. His words were sharp, like someone poking my cheeks, and he could have either been thanking us for our business or informing us that the brakes had been cut and we were hurtling towards an unfinished bridge. Further down the car I spied an entire row of sleeping businessmen. An old woman with purple hair. A TV with high-color freakout images flashing across the screen. One commercial stated "MAKE WOW" in neon pink bubbles. Only twenty minutes in the country and the conceptual aesthetic of Nintendo made much more sense to me. The cartoons, colors, and bubblegum excitement were drawn from a deeper well here and exported to us via video game.

Soon we were spit out of the train and onto the dark, wet streets. Clear umbrellas. People everywhere. Again, I am jarred by being a head taller than anyone around. Buildings stacked against each other, filled with people, flush with business. Restaurants with men in ties eating alone. Plates of sushi trundling around a conveyor belt.

My precisely-written instructions did not fail me, and after a few orienting turns I found the hotel. While checking in I asked the clerk where I could get something to eat and he suggested a "good" pizza place around the corner. Like I had come to Japan to eat pizza. We took the elevator to the sixth floor and walked down a narrow hallway with two stacked rows of 3x3 foot squares on one side, lockers on the other. At the 8th column he pointed to the square on the bottom: my home for the next few days. This was a capsule hotel, meaning that instead of a room I rented a 7x3x3 foot cube which had a mattress, shelf and small TV. It was possible to both sit and lie down, but that was about it. Fifty of these cubicles fit in the space of three normal hotel rooms.

Forgoing the idea of Japanese pizza at this hour (what hour? It was night but beyond that I still didn't know), I stuffed my bag into the locker and climbed into the capsule, sparking a strange and laughable feeling. It was, in my jetlagged mind, much like a honey bee in her cell. Inside, and with the curtain closed, the sensation intensified. I was a pupating larva.

I turned on the TV, a luxury the bees do not yet have. Newscasters spoke in odd, knife-edge tones. In a commercial for soup, the can grew eyes, popped a speech bubble and did a flip. I was on the sixth of eight floors, with dozens or hundreds of other cells around me. I wondered what the next day would bring, when we all uncapped our cells and began to work about the hive.

While visiting Manabu in the city of Hamamatsu, I searched the internet for Japanese beekeepers and found the website of the Ginza Honey project. I contacted them, asking if I could visit and write an article on them, and to my delight they agreed to meet the day before my flight to Australia. However, when I walked up the stairs of the subway station they directed me to and found myself on a street with Prada, Gucci and dozens of other stores with far too many zeros at the end of their price tags, I had strong doubts that I was in the right place.

It would not have been the first time in Tokyo when I navigated the lines of the psychedelic spaghetti only to realize that a different subway company (yes, there are multiple, overlapping subway systems) had a stop with the same name but on the opposite side of the city. Was this Ginza—Tokyo's version of Fifth Avenue—the place they kept bees?

Two women wearing bee suits in the lobby of a nearby office building answered my question. They bowed as I reached out to shake, I, once again, forgetting the Japanese custom, and then attempted an awkward bow in return. One woman was Kei, the project's beekeeper, and the other Yukiko, Kei's friend came as a translator. We stumbled over our introductions and small talk—Yukiko finding her English and I remembering to speak slowly and use uncomplicated words. One of the first bits of information we shared was our mutual surprise at our youth—with all of us in our late 20s, both sides thought they would be meeting someone much older.

We boarded the elevator and Kei pressed the button for the top floor. Talk sputtered and information came in blobs as each of us accustomed to our role: presenter, translator and interviewer. Confusion reigned, and I had to keep circling back to answers I didn't understand, or rewording phrases that seemed to be mangled in the translation process. Sometimes the two women talked in Japanese for a long time and answered a different question than I had asked. I scribbled down notes but could already tell the article I wanted to write would have some significant holes. We were in the era when Google Translate had just gained traction, and Yukiko had it out constantly to look up words during her translation. When I asked about honey sources in the area, she typed something in her phone and pointed the screen at me: "Common Lime," it read "They have it in Chicago," she added.

Kei wasn't the founder of the Ginza project. Someone else, but he wasn't available. From what I could tell, taking care of these ten hives was Kei's job. Maybe it was a full-time job. It seemed there were multiple beekeepers employed taking care of these ten hives. The project had won some awards. It was a non-profit. It was trying to promote coexistence of urban and natural environments. They sold every drop of honey they made. It was used in cocktails at a local bar. They also had rooftop gardens.

The view from the roof showed urban canyons in every direction. Some trees lined the sidewalk, but the bees' important foraging grounds were the Imperial Palace gardens, an urban green area within foraging distance. Yukiko told me that the Imperial Palace gardens was worth more than all of California. Kei brought out a bee suit and asked if I wanted to use it. The cuffs would have landed at my knees. I declined.

143

Four hives stood together on one corner of the roof. Kei lit a smoker and started a routine inspection. We looked at the brood, eggs, and bees. One of the hives was smaller than a Langstroth and held *Apis cerana*. Kei did not use smoke on these bees for fear they would abscond—abandon the hive en masse to find a new home. She continued through the rest of the hives. At one point she opened a bottle of bright blue liquid and poured it into the feeder. As I was trying to get Yukiko to ask Kei about that windshield-wiper-looking stuff, the skies opened and it began to pour. There hadn't even been a warning drizzle. Yukiko and I fled to a small overhang and Kei, after closing up the hive, soon followed. We laughed, already soaked, and it dawned on me we were trapped: a stretch of fierce rain and uncovered rooftop stood between us and the elevator. As we waited for the weather to ease, I unearthed more questions to fill my article's blank spots and Yukiko and Kei tried to coordinate answers.

After a few minutes the rain slowed and we hustled across the roof towards the elevator. By the time we descended to the lobby, the rain had stopped and pedestrians put away their umbrellas. At that point, Yukiko and Kei made an amazing Superman-Clark Kent switch where by taking off their coveralls they transformed from beekeepers to chic city women. We walked across an avenue and into the basement of a shopping center which held a market of artisanal (and mostly Western) foodstuffs. We passed stacks of freshly baked breads, rainbow rows of macaroons, truffle oils, chocolates, and wines. Eventually we arrived at a honey stall which offered jars from everywhere in the world: Corsica, Canada, New Zealand, Chile and more. They also sold pure Ginza honey in thirty-six gram jars, about the size of a shot, for 1680 yen. While in Tokyo I was used to roughly translating prices in my head, about 80 yen to a dollar, and though I was used to everything being slightly more expensive, I had to do the mental math twice to understand that this little jar cost $21. The Ginza Project had harvested 840 kg of honey the previous year. I wasn't ready to tackle that math, but it began to make sense how this handful of hives, and the growing desire for the wealthy to buy local foods, could support multiple beekeepers in this project.

After being given a jar of Ginza gold (for that price was about two meals in my budget, and tasted indistinguishable from any other basswood honey that has crossed my palate), we moved to a nearby restaurant for lunch. I had been the one asking questions all morning, so as we sat down the spotlight flipped and I came under inquiry: they did not understand what I did and why I was here. I explained that I was a freelance beekeeper working for large-scale queen breeders and honey producers around the world. I would work for six to nine months during the spring and summer and then travel during the off season. These concepts were completely foreign to them, as I could deduce from their low-pitched moans of amazement. As I told them about grafting thousands of queen cells, and trucking hundreds of hives around the country for pollination, I realized that this probably sounded as strange to them as the bright-blue feeding liquid or the price of Ginza honey seemed to me.

After the meal ended we walked out to the street under a clear sun. We smiled at each other, stumbling over thank yous and farewells, our group standing like a stone on the sidewalk while the stream of people flowed around us. Just as we were both about to slip back into the Tokyo current, I put my arms to my sides and did my best bow. Kei, instead, stuck out her hand to shake.

23

Australian Road

2012

Warren's office held an L-shaped desk with seven inches of paper detritus covering its surface. With a little digging one could probably find a printer somewhere in there, and probably an endless number of pens and staplers, but mostly it seemed to consist of old phone books, overstuffed manila folders, and bills. Without organization, seven inches seemed to be the maximum height before papers would start sliding to the floor (and the floor was surprisingly clean), but the most fascinating part to me was the generic wall clock sticking out of one of the piles. Its incessant ticking was the only sound in the room, yet the clock always read 2:35. The smallest hand shuddered every second but couldn't break free from its spot, leaving the other hands frozen in time.

When I walked out of the guest room at 7 AM, Warren was already in his office, coffee in hand, talking to someone on the phone. The phone was the only thing I ever saw Warren use in there. He would sit behind the piles of paper, punch out a number, and suddenly be asking someone on the other side of the state about the yellow box flow, or setting up an order of queens, or swapping gossip. When I heard his deep belly laugh, I knew I would be hearing a new joke sometime later that day.

After jostling for the bathroom with Warren's kids, Anthony age 12 and Niki age 15, we settled down together for a lethargic bowl of cereal before they ran to the school bus. With the house quiet, I gathered my gear, Warren watered his plastic bin of radishes, and we met in front of the house when we were both ready.

The old two-ton flatbed looked odd parked on this prim, suburban street of Bathurst. I am sure the neighbors had a few things to say about its frequent presence, and I could imagine the homeowners association delicately trying to word a law that would limit the presence of work vehicles in the neighborhood. The handful of confused bees constantly circling around it probably didn't help either. When we both climbed in the truck and drove away, the bees would circle for a while longer before clustering on the mailbox, wondering what to do next.

It was on these days, riding with Warren, that I probably learned the most practical knowledge of my beekeeping career. With thick, white eyebrows, sideburns, and a half-combed nest of hair, Warren was around 60 years old and still going strong. Over the decades he went from driving hives around the continent on his own to having over a dozen employees and thousands of hives—the largest operation in Australia. Beekeeping in Australia requires a lot of driving—there are no short rides—and on the trips we rode together I had all day to pick Warren's brain for the gems of his lifetime of beekeeping practice.

"You need to be a botanist to be an Australian beekeeper," he told me as we settled into our journey. Producing a successful honey crop In Australia is like playing chess. The country has dozens of honey flows from their native eucalyptus species—box trees (white, yellow, red, fuzzy), gum trees (blue, spotted, white, red river), stringybark, ironwood, leatherwood, mallee—the list is surprisingly long. At any point in the year, flowers are blooming somewhere on the continent. It becomes a matter of having the locations, understanding the weather and plants, preparing the bees, and crunching the economic and logistical numbers.

Warren had hammered down this process over his career. It required a strong working memory and a detailed attention to the weather both at home and beyond. Certain plants are affected by the rainfall from the previous year, or by nighttime temperatures in the spring, or the proper amount of winter sunshine, which are easy enough all easy enough to pay attention to outside your window, but it takes a good network to keep track of multiple far-flung locations around the continent. Warren had a huge number of contacts and knew how to read the signs. "It's gonna be a good year for the Ironbark," he growled.

"How do you know?"

"Look at the buds," he pointed at the tree we had just whipped by at 70 MPH. I only saw leaves.

From Bathurst we began passing through the same parade of towns with names that seemed to come from bottom-of-the-barrel *Lord of the Rings* fan fiction: Bathurst, Orange, Brocklehurst, Mudgie, Dubbo, Glugong, Bimbi, Manildra, Whylanria. On the edge of these towns stood welcome signs that gave me endless pleasure: Gilgandra, The Place of Many Rocks; Molong, The Home of World Friendship; Canowindra, The Town that Time Forgot. When we stopped in one of these burgs to pick up a turkey and beetroot sandwich, someone at the store said hi to Warren. "Good rain coming, 'init? How the bees? Good on ya, them Cockies got some whooshie honey this year. Bogged down, huh?" the Aussie platitudes batted deftly back and forth like a hot badminton match until the man took off with his own sandwich and Warren turned to me and said, "I have no idea who that was."

We drove further and further inland. Three hours from our home base—which itself was a few hours from the coast—we passed a sign that said "Halfway to the Outback." Towns grew further apart and the landscape dried up. Road trains—trucks dragging three full trailers behind them—flew straight at us on narrowing roads and both parties, without slowing down, edged their outside wheels over the crumbling lip to pass each other before taking the whole road again. Warren's phone rang. "Yup, yeah ... &!@#," he grumbled, and then hung up. Twenty minutes later he pulled across a cattle gate and stopped in front of a run-down farmhouse with worn-out bee equipment stacked haphazardly around the back. He knocked on the door and soon we had a steaming cuppa in front of us, chatting with this old fellow about the weather and swapping stories about other beekeepers ("You think Wayne's gone up to yellow string this year?") After the cuppa went down, Warren parted with a joke he probably learned on the phone that morning ("So Julia Gillard walks into a bar ..."), and we hit the road again, heading west, towards the deep red outback.

This trip inland was a part of Warren's latest plan: selling Aussie comb honey to the Chinese. Green mallee is a shrub in the outback that produces a magnificent honey which never crystallizes. Warren believed that the Chinese, who live in constant fear of food tampering, would happily pay a pretty Yuan for clean Australian green mallee honey. Though success on both the production and exportation was uncertain, Warren loved a challenge. Challenges were what kept him going. Driving together for hours, I began to glean into Warren's thought process. Though bath time was his preferred spot for rumination, in the truck he would work through the idea by throwing the questions in the air, sometimes repeating himself from a few hours earlier, as if a bit more oxygen would help the solution pop.

The challenges, I realized, were less about the bees and more about the bee business. Though a knowledgeable and good beekeeper he most certainly was, Warren focused on his competition in the industry as much as his bees. His latest object was giving "those Hawaiians" (the beekeepers I had once worked for) "a run for their money" by shipping queens and packages to the mainland USA. With a twinkle in his eye, he'd add, "Just wait until I have both of their testicles in my hand." This, I realized, was what it took to be a big player in the bee industry. Actually, in any industry. Those thinking like this naturally rose to the top and held the reins of influence.

As the angle of the sun changed, the colors deepened, and the landscape became kinder. We passed a family of emus—mom and three chicks—standing in a golden field of wheat. At dusk kangaroos began to appear, hopping across the road while their dimmer kin lay in bloody mounds of meat on the road. "Here in Australia, we eat our national symbol," Warren was fond of saying. I stuck my head out the window into the full whipping wind to get a full view of the sun crashing down on the hills ahead of us. The joy of this made my heart nearly burst. When I brought my head back in Warren grumbled "A romantic, huh?" The radio took a break from music for a news report: fires in Northern New South Wales, which after a week of burning out of control, had finally been contained, while heavy rains in Southern New South Wales were causing raging floods and washing away farmhouses and livestock alike. It seemed a pity that rains and the fire didn't coordinate. The next day we would have a high 38°C. (100.4°F.)

After a good seven hours on the road, we pulled into a driveway with a locked gate. Warren handed me the key and, after passing through it, we came upon a beekeeper loading hives onto the back of his truck with a boom crane. Warren stopped the truck and we both stepped out and stretched.

"How we doing lad?" Warren yelled.

"Crikey, Warren," David yelled back. "Why'd you come today? Everything was going good until today."

David was about the same age as Warren, but thinner, taller and without much hair. This was his property, and we had put a hundred hives on the other side of the dry creek. Greetings aside, we let David finish loading, got back in the truck and drove a hundred meters to David's small cabin. After throwing down our swags (an Australian term for a one-piece tent/sleeping bag), Warren lit the fire and we had a giant heap of grilled meat ready by the time David joined us. Sitting at the table with a couple of empty and full Victoria Bitters, and a framed picture of a tractor tacked to the wall behind them, the Aussie beekeepers traded old-men barbs:

"Oh," David said, standing up to get another beer, "I'm going to be stiff all week."

"Yeah, well your wife will like that." Warren cackled. The bug zapper buzzed with the death of a mosquito.

Bottles empty, bottles full.

"You bring them on to Red Box this year?" Warren asked David, wringing a grim grin from the man. It was a long-running joke that David once brought his bees to make a honey crop from Red Box trees, which bloom late in the fall and produce a nice honey but not much pollen. Without pollen the colonies can't raise new bees to replace the aging foragers and will "fly their guts out" until they essentially collapse. David lost seventy-odd hives from that incident, and apparently will never live it down. The two of them then dragged out a few more hard-up beekeeper tales: 120 of 150 hives dead after plum and cherry pollination in the north. Crop failure and starving colonies in the desert. Pesticide sprays and truck accidents. Tales of apicultural woe.

"Dirty work this beekeeping," David said.

"You know, the art of beekeeping," Warren added, "is getting your hives in the peak condition on the right flow."

Another sage nugget of this profession floating freely into the night air. We were three beekeepers sitting on a porch, sweaty and dusty, drinking beer, miles away from any form of civilization. A long day had ended, and another long day lay ahead. Now on my nth beer, my head felt lighter, and I was about ready to crawl into my stale but comfortable swag for a sleep under the bright moon. With my hand in my pocket I felt a metal bolt. I had no idea how it got there.

The bug zapper went haywire, frying a bug for a good five seconds.

"Here's one for you, David," Warren announced. "So Julia Gillard walks into a bar..."

24

Australian Wind

2012

The days followed a mirror-like pattern. We drove to a bee yard somewhere on the edge of the outback, strapped a metal belt around each hive so it could be easily moved in one piece, and then waited until sunset for the bees to return home. Then we loaded each hives by hand onto the truck; there were no Bobcats or pallets in this operation, you merely "bobbed down and picked it up," as Ralph said. Two of us on the ground tipped a hive at an angle and then hoisted the 100+ pounds box to carry it to the truck. We'd angle the bottom to hit the corner of the four-foot-tall bed, and then pushed the hive as the man on the bed pulled and arranged it in place. Once the bed was full, we began adding the next row on top of the first, hoisting the heavy hives seven feet off the dust. Sometimes there would even be a third level running like a spine down the middle of the top, but these were usually small hives that were easy to lift overhead. If we were smart, we would load the very heavy hives as the bottom row, but it was hard being smart while sweating in the thick evening air.

The bees stung, the backs hurt, the pits sweat, the fingers got smashed, the arms grew tired. We usually threw the nets over just as it got too dark to see, with the final twenty minutes of work being illuminated by shining headlights, like at a forest party or a murder scene. Then we drove about four hours deeper into the outback (though where we started was considered "front country", it was still twenty minutes of pure brush between each town) grabbing dinner and a beer at a dingy diner on the way. Arriving deep in the bush close to the witching hour, we parked the truck, threw down a swag, took off the boots and dipped into a few hours of sleep. At daybreak, somewhere south of 6 AM, we woke, packed swags, and unloaded the bees right where we had been sleeping. Once again the pits sweat, the backs hurt, the bees stung, the fingers got smashed, the arms grew tired. Then we drove four hours back to the first location, where many hives still remained, stopping somewhere for a bad sandwich, a grimy truck-stop shower, and generally killing time until sunset.

We had repeated the above for five days in a row, Ralph, Jorge and I. Ralph was a suspender-wearing sixty-five-year-old Australian bloke with shocking gray eyes. He had a busted knee (making him pick up heavy hives exactly as one is instructed not to: bending straight at the waist and making my back hurt just watching him) and had essentially retired, but kept getting roped back into these bee moves as he was friends with the boss and the only one who had a truck license. All other members of the operation either didn't have a truck license or had been ruled out due to their horrible driving records. One of the

latter, banned from the driver's seat for life, was Jorge, or George as the Aussies liked to translate. George was a heart-sick young Peruvian who had gotten into three car accidents in the two months I had been there, one of which happened because he while was fixing his hair in the rear view mirror, instead of turning with the road, he drove straight off a six-foot embankment into a cow pasture, rolling three times and coming to rest in a smoking, crinkled scrapheap. The truck was totaled and the insurance company threatened to cancel the entire company's plan, but George (and the cows in the pasture) walked away unharmed.

Finally, finally, this evening we were on the home stretch. Though we had worked through the weekend, and we would likely dive straight into Monday morning without a break, at least we would be back in beds, with a shower that didn't stink of a ripe outback trucker. It was late, close to midnight, and I was smashed between Ralph and George in the truck's middle seat, all of us staring straight ahead. Every time Ralph shifted gears meant I had to shift my body into George's, and then a relax back into the free space, knee touching buzzing stick shift.

Conversation had flagged a few days prior, and now we only said the necessities. The droning of the motor was our constant, the sparse parade of small towns with squat, brick houses our visual stimulant, and the radio our color—spinning classics and commercials in a nearly even ratio. And in one moment, Bette Midler's "Wind Beneath my Wings" poured through the speakers. "Did you ever know that you're my hero?" Bette crooned in impossibly heavy syrup. What an epic, absurd song. I waited for some sort of comment—a laugh or scoff from my ride-mates—but neither said a thing, so I didn't either. No one reached for the radio dial. "I could fly higher than an eagle..." We listened to the whole tune in silence. Maybe they didn't even notice it, or it just slipped past them like a ghost, but it slapped me in the face and I felt like I was going to burst—the three of us shoulder-to-shoulder, the overwhelming days of work, the weariness, and the absurd song all piled together into a few precious, unfathomable minutes.

Then the song ended. A commercial for an Italian restaurant came on. The lights of Bathurst rose in the distance. We were almost home.

25

Drones

Drones are funny creatures. With oversized heads and giant wings, they have a cylindrical body like a well-stuffed burrito. People often admire honey bees for their work ethic and orderliness, but those people are not thinking of the drones, who only make up about 10% of a colony. Drones, brothers of the worker bees, are the opposite of the above stereotypes. They are the bumbling oafs of the bee world.

Drones are lazy. They do none of the endless chores required to make the hive run. They clamber about the comb, loud and clumsy, begging the busy worker bees to give them food. If rejected enough times, they will eventually help themselves to some honey, which is in the comb directly beneath their feet. Their only job is to hang around outside on sunny days and try to mate with passing queens.

Nine times out of ten, when I give this lecture to an audience of families, the moms will twitter and chuckle, turning to the dads with a comment like, "that sounds familiar." The husbands will shrug and reply, "Yup." By that point of the lecture the kids will already be poking each other or rolling on the floor, waiting for the boring man to stop talking.

However, the drone is excellent at his one job. When a virgin queen flies by, he spots her with his massive eyes and then chases her with his strong wings, competing with the other drones who have similar strengths and are all after the same thing. The fastest and most agile drone who reachers her first will mate with the queen in mid-air. This is his well-defined peak in life: after the moment of coupling, his phallus detaches to stay inside the queen (temporarily deterring the other drones who are lining up behind him), and he tumbles to the earth, deceased in his moment of fulfillment, the purest definition of ecstasy.

The husbands of the audience then might wipe their brows and say that they're glad that doesn't happen to them. Wait a moment, I tell them, for the drones that perish here are actually the lucky ones.

Those that don't mate with a queen and don't get eaten by a bird continue their lives of luxury throughout the summer: dining on the finest honey and loafing about with their buddies along the edge of some glorious meadow. When the days grow shorter and the nights get colder, a feeling among their sisters begins to grow. These guys, their genes tell them, are not dragging their weight. One day, after another unsuccessful afternoon, the drones return to the hive hungry for dinner. At the landing board, rather than give way, the guard bees stand strong, blocking the entrance. The drones, confused by the sudden switch, try to climb inside their home again and again, but the sisters who fed them the day before no longer have any mercy. The sun is setting and the temperature dropping. Those drones still in the hive are dragged out and dumped onto the ground with the others. They might try to enter a neighboring colony, but their cousins were dealt a similar fate: the long dearth of winter had arrived and a drone's presence would offer nothing to the colony's survival. They would be just another mouth to feed during the difficult cold period, when an extra ounce of honey could mean the difference between the colony's life and death. That night, in the open air and without the warmth of their sisters and family, the drones perish: cold, alone, and unfulfilled.

Sometimes when working through a yard, I'll take a drone and put it inside my veil. A worker bee inside here could sting my face, but a dim little drone has no weapon. Confused, he will amble about my protected zone, jumping to fly, banging into the mesh, falling down, climbing on my cheek, buzzing in annoyance. He keeps me company as I look through hive after hive. When the yard is done, I take off my veil and let him crawl out. He waits a moment and then jumps into the air, dissolving into the cloud of the hundreds of other bees circling above the yard, heading back to his hive or the meadow's edge. I hope the minutes spent with me somehow inspire his duty towards the hive. I always wish him good luck.

157

26

Australian Beeline

2012

The sun beat straight through my wide-brimmed straw hat. Diane and I stood together, still, waiting. Two line-workers, who were pulling concrete or some other hard material off a rumbling conveyor belt in a warehouse thirty yards away, eyed us and swapped comments when their stream of work slowed. The industrial noise prevented me from hearing, but I read their smirks. Diane and I, in our matching orange and blue uniforms, screamed "government work," and our current activity, which looked very much like nothing at all, didn't help. It had been over twenty minutes since an iota of action. Glancing at the workers, I envied their shade. At the moment I would have cut off my pinky for a cool drink.

Diane and I were bee-lining *Apis cerana* in Cannes, Australia. I had taken a week off from queen production in New South Wales to volunteer for Biosecurity Queensland's "Transition to Management" program. *Apis cerana* is a honey bee native to much of Asia. It is a smaller and less productive bee than *Apis mellifera*, the European honey bee, which is the accepted non-native honey bee in Australia. (As in America, Australia did not originally have honey bees, so they could be considered invasive.) Because of a growth in ocean traffic during the past few decades, it hasn't been uncommon for a colony of *cerana* to arrive as a stowaway in some crack or crevice of a container ship. Usually the colony is starving, weak and unable to make very much of itself after a few weeks at sea, but they have the potential to squeak through. In 2008 a *cerana* colony was found in the mast of a yacht that had been in dry dock for eighteen months. Over the next eighteen months a dozen of its daughter colonies were discovered on land. Biosecurity Queensland (BSQL) went into overdrive to try to eradicate the incursion, with the Cannes port being ground zero.

Luckily, the swarm did not bring the varroa mite, but for five years the eradication of *A. cerana* was still the goal. Government eradicators hunted down and destroyed dozens of nests, but more always appeared in an ever-expanding geographical range. When I arrived for the volunteer session in 2012, BSQL had just accepted that eradication was impossible and had renamed the operation "Transition to Management", with new goals of limiting the spread and learning how to coexist with it. On the day I showed up, I announced that I wanted to write an article for *American Bee Journal* about the Asian honey bee in Australia. This sent the office into a small frenzy, and I was soon invited to a meeting with the program's director and PR rep. The situation, I found out, was also a bit political. The big fuss was the potential of the Asian honey bee migrating naturally or by human means to the queen breeding areas of New South Wales, interbreeding with European honey bees, and thus invalidating the country's international queen export business. Though they couldn't force me to do anything, I left the meeting with the feeling that I would have to choose my words carefully. I still had some months left in the country, and making enemies was never high on my list of things to do in an international situation.

The initial edge of excitement quickly dulled with the transition into work. This consisted of highly stimulating jobs like combing through a pile of dead bees to separate drones from workers, watching hours of video footage of a hive entrance and counting the foragers that leave the hive, or bee-lining.

Bee-lining is a method of finding a colony in the wild. The basic steps are: 1. put out a bowl of floral-scented sugar water which will attract bees, 2. wait for a scout bee to check it out (this step can take a very long time, or might not happen at all), 3. watch the scout bee drink the sugar water, 4. observe the direction the scout flies (bees really do fly back to their nest in a dead-straight line), 5. move the bowl five or ten paces in that direction, 6. wait for the scout to return with other foragers to harvest the sugar water, 7. repeat steps 2-6 until you see the location of the colony, which could be any small, dry cavity from a hollow tree to a mailbox to an upside-down bathtub.

Humans have been lining honey bees since ancient times. When I first read about the process, my imagination took a romantic turn; I could a sparsely clothed hunter-gatherer waiting patiently among hot desert rocks, squinting at one wall of a box canyon, his afternoon almost gone but feeling the success grow close as his chunk of honeycomb, from the last conquest, is swarmed over by the wild bees. They carry heavy loads of this new-found treasure towards some nook in the canyon wall that the hunter will soon gain full knowledge of and pull out dripping handfuls of brood and wax to bring home in celebration.

Not so here. We were standing in the dusty driveway of some sort of soulless industrial park. The conveyor belt rumbled without cease, broken chunks of something streamed through, the economy pushed along. Soon a truck drove past us and for ten minutes I watched the driver try, and fail, to back his trailer into a narrow stall. It was like watching the worst TV show in the world.

But suddenly I saw Diane tense and a flash of movement around the sugar dish. We both leaned down to spy on a small, striped *Apis cerana* tasting the sugar and sand mixture under the plastic awning. How had she found this spot? I try to imagine the process of a scout bee leaving her hive and searching the landscape for food. This pot of ours certainly didn't look like a flower, but it must have been throwing out enough scent particles for her sensitive antennae to catch as they flew by.

After drinking deeply, the scout sprang into the air, circled around us, and flew directly towards a labyrinth of stacked cinder blocks, some already leaning on their neighbors, others looking like they would topple on and maim any trespasser at the next strong gust of wind. Behind the labyrinth was a junkyard of old cars. Both were a heaven for bee nesting sites and a hell for anyone trying to locate them.

"Could be anywhere," Diane sighed as we moved the table towards the cinder blocks. "Sometimes it takes five minutes, other times it takes days." But by then our minutes had just about run out. We left the table where it stood and drove across town for our next chore: to count the number of *A. cerana* drones leaving a feral nest in five-minute intervals. I kept an eye on the watch as Diane stared directly at a hole in the rafter of a garage where a bee would pop out every few seconds. After that we had just enough time to do a lap around the city before heading to the office to punch out.

Another day of government work: done.

27

Australian Grind

2012

At breakfast Neneth and I move around each other in the kitchen like ghosts. We say good morning but that's it, at least until we start working and need to speak at a functional level. I pour some yogurt on my oatmeal and stare at nothing while spooning it into my mouth. She juggles three pans on the two working burners, one of them frying something hot and filling the house with meat-smell. Maybe she is making the dish made of pig's blood, intestines and lemongrass that I tried last week. It was actually pretty good, but not what I want to breathe at 6:15 AM.

I ask Lauro how to do something. Something like, when tying down the truck, do I put the supporters on the back of the load or only half-way back? I usually need to ask him twice. Yeah, that's right, he replies, in the vaguest way possible. I pick what I thought he said, but half the time someone else comes by to tell me it's wrong. Lauro's worked at this company for eight years but only does enough not to get yelled at. He's married to Neneth, who is cousin to Rose, our boss. We live in the bunkhouse together—Lauro, Neneth, and myself. They make their Australian dollars and send them back to the Philippines, and then visit once per year during the slow season. Lauro's first questions to me were: What nationality are you? You have your citizenship? You were born there, but your parents weren't? You want citizenship here?

Underneath those questions is the one he doesn't ask: What are you doing here?

The syrup room is the size of a garage. We line the concrete floor with cans, end to end, so over a hundred cans fit inside the room at once. Someone operates the valve and fills the cans with sugar syrup one at a time. Another moves the full cans away and makes sure there are more empty cans within reach. A third puts lids on the full cans. A fourth, if there was a fourth, pounds the lids tight with a hammer. During this process, which can last a few hours, we are constantly crouching. Knees are sore, backs ache, necks kink. We each have our task, we each focus on completing it. Honey bees do the same thing. When the hundred cans are full and capped, we stand in a bucket brigade and pass the cans outside to the truck. Then we line the floors with empty cans once again and switch tasks. The relief from losing the previous task's strain is quickly overshadowed by the pain created from the new task. Each job has its pain. Jeans stiffen with sugar, boots whiten and shine. Later in the day, when I take off my clothes, my skin is sweet.

There are around ten of us working together. Two Peruvians, two Moldovans, a rotating handful of Filipinos, one Hungarian and myself. No Australians, strangely. Or maybe it's not so strange. We work seven days a week, Monday to Monday, or at least we need to count on working every day, and any free day we can take as a pleasant surprise. Any Aussie who wants to have a life wouldn't want to do this work. We usually get a half-day off on Sundays. On that afternoon we compete for the laundry machine and make a group trip into town for groceries. For the first month I kept track of my hours. I didn't get paid by the hour, and after writing down two eighty-hour weeks in a row, totaling the time got depressing, and I stopped.

I had lived in a fair share of crummy bunkhouses, but Black Springs was by far the worst. I was the first to arrive and opened the bunkhouse's door to find that the hasty exit from last year's crew had gone stale and mutated. A graveyard of flies on the window sill. Small black piles which looked like seeds but upon closer inspection were revealed to be curled bodies of dead ants. "10 cap, 7 win abc, prime" written in marker on a wall. A pair of soiled, men's underwear over the shower door. Miscellaneous trash, broken wood, and grime at every turn. A lonely can of orange juice concentrate in the cupboard, expired three years. In the fridge a rash of black mold, in the crisper, a forgotten head of cauliflower blooming into a science experiment. In the freezer a half inch of warm water with chunks of fish skin. Inside a plastic bag on the table, another plastic bag. Inside that, an explosion of green and white mold, the odor unbelievable. I picked it up and threw it out the front door, onto the lawn. I followed a trail of ants along the kitchen floor to a bottom cupboard where inside I saw a black, five-pound bucket of honey. The black was strangely textured, and a closer inspection showed movement. The thing was nearly knuckle-deep in ants, and their hard months of gnawing through the plastic top looked like it paid off. I opened the front door, put on an oven mitt and threw this monstrosity onto the front lawn, followed by the oven mitt itself. After that, I didn't know where to begin.

Black Springs is about five hours from Sydney. It is an hour from Bathurst, a small city which is familiar to anyone into the Australian car-racing circuit. Bathurst's center looks like it has had a few saloon shootouts in its day. I could easily imagine the snap of a rifle shot and a villain tumbling off the top of a building. Once you travel that extra hour to Black Springs, you aren't greeted with much. It has a crossroads and a closed gas station. It is near the Blue Mountains National Park, which I hear is nice. I'd like to go check it out, but we don't have any time.

Lauro likes the TV show *Deal or No Deal.* Sometimes I watch it with him when I'm waiting for my turn in the kitchen, and exhaustion ties me to the couch. Lauro sits in the easy chair and puts his feet up. When the contestant takes a low deal, Lauro grunts and changes the channel to Philippine news.

Like in any seasonal bunkhouse, the feeling of transience invades every corner. Too many bodies, too tired to care, too happy to leave when the season is over. Leftover clothing shoved in a garbage bag on the couch. Paint chips falling off the ceiling. A stovetop with burners that only function on high. Three jars of Coffee-Mate on the dining table in varying degrees of fullness. A laundry room with powdered soap spilled everywhere and a creeping black mold on the walls. A plastic kid's table between the chair and the TV. Dirt-streaked walls. An old camera on a shelf. Marker drawn on a wall from a child many years earlier. Elsewhere, the marker a little higher, as if the child grew and continued marking. A listless karaoke machine. The bathroom door unhinged. A pile of stained mattresses in the back yard. A calendar, hanging cockeyed, two months and two years out of date. A circle pattern of holes around the outline of a former dartboard. A row of empty Johnny Walker Blue whiskey bottles on a shelf.

Griping is a part of the daily routine every day. Depending on who I ride with, the subject changes. Ride with the bosses and I hear about the employees' shortcomings: they don't care about the company, don't put the right effort into the work, and don't understand the pressure required to make the right business choices to stay afloat against the competition. The more you give them, the more they take. In the employee truck I hear a different story: the bosses don't understand what it like working long hours for someone who yells at you out of frustration, getting a paycheck without a future, and not feeling in control of anything in life. The tension is string-taut and we spend many hours a day working together. Everyone complains. We don't know the other's shoes.

Laying in my bed, I listen to a lecture by the philosopher Alan Watts. He says we are not separate from the universe. We are expressions of it. There are no such things as things, that is to say separate things, or separate events. If you can understand this, he says, you will have no further problems.

I could be anywhere in all of eternity. But I exist here in this moment. This is me.

I maintain a keen interest in the ongoing insect infestation of the bunkhouse. Spiders rule the upper corners while the ants control everything else. Flies the size of grapes appear out of some unseen mag-goty cove. Multiple webs dot each corner, and I imagine the spider neighbors admire each other's handicraft. These are the ones I can see. What's happening in the hidden corners of stacked boxes in the living room, I can't imagine. It is a universe I will never enter. The bathroom is the battleground I am most interested in. A spider with long, thin legs has lived above the shower for weeks. One morning I see it spinning a fly's body round and round and round. I stand on a stool to get a closer look. The spider pauses as I draw near, but then continues to spin.

Lauro and Neneth have a strong affinity for Tom Jones. On the living room stereo it is usually either his greatest hits CD, or another album called, "Unforgettable Enchantment." If I hear either of these, I retreat to my room with earplugs or go for a walk. Oddly, I have yet to see the karaoke machine put in action. I have heard that Filipinos love kara-oke. I have also heard that in the Philippines there have been a series of murders against people singing painful karaoke versions of Frank Sinatra's, "My Way".

Bees have a set progression of tasks in their life. When a worker is born, she immediately begins cleaning the cell in which she pupated to allow the queen to use it once again. After a few days of cell cleaning, she becomes a nurse bee, feeding the growing larvae a special secre-tion from her body called "worker jelly". After that her body begins to produce wax, which she will use to repair comb or build new cells, her frontal legs the perfect calipers for creating that hexagonal struc-ture. From there a few more stages follow—attending the queen, nec-tar receiving, honey sealing, pollen packing, removing dead bees and detritus, propolizing, guarding—but the final stage of the worker's life is foraging. The bee will fly from hive to flower, over and over, until she is eaten by a predator or her wings wear out. If she is born in the late fall and there is no foraging to be done, she can live for the entire winter. If she is born in the summer, her lifespan will last a matter of weeks. A bee's wings are only able to fly a certain number of miles. Then life is over.

The phone rings. I put down my book, get out of bed and walk to the living room.

"Is Neneth there?" It's Rose.

"Nope. She went out."

"Anyway..." Rose replies, and hangs up.

Every morning I wake up at 5:30 AM without an alarm. I make a cup of tea and spend the first forty-five minutes of my day reading. When I get home at night I make dinner. About twice a week I get in the car and drive a few hundred yards to the top of a rise where I can get phone signal and check my email. Then I go back to the bunkhouse and read. My stack of books is high, and I'm flying through them.

We are filling syrup cans again. I hammer one can shut, then the next, then the next. You went to an esteemed school, I heard a voice say, you paid lots of money for it. Your schoolmates are becoming doctors and lawyers right now. You deserve better than this.

No you don't, another voice breaks in. You've snuck through everything your whole life. You sucked at school. You got in because your mom worked there, then you got into the next one because you were a good athlete but then you quit. You're not very smart. All you know how to do is work hard, be pleasant, and be open to new experiences. You deserve this. Syrup flies into my face. You're an ass, the voice continues. You're a pretentious ass.

Rose, our boss, is not a woman you want to mess with. Her temper is short, she always looks as if she's in a bad mood, and she yells at certain bumbling employees as a vent for her frustration. Yet, I admire her. She has a singular determination which got her to this position in life: coming from a poor background in the Philippines, she took the frightening leap of migrating alone to Australia and battled though creepy bosses, crappy jobs, and the cultural shock of being far from home. One day, having never worked with bees, she began grafting queens. She worked her way up the ladder. Eventually she married Warren, our other boss. Now Warren deals with the honey production while Rose singlehandedly runs the biggest queen-rearing operation in Australia, selling quality queens to beekeepers around the world and employing an untold number of her cousins.

"You need a goal in life," she tells me one time when we are driving together, as she is reflecting on her own. I take this advice to heart.

I am the syrup pouring into these tins, being splashed on the floor, mixing with the rust. I am the atoms between the sugar and the water. I am its brown color as we pour it in the hive. The bees are happy. They hope only for nectar, pollen, shelter and a queen to take care of. My hopes are grand, wide, and beyond my reach. The bees hope for nothing. They are little programmed robots acting on their external stimuli. I open up the lid and one stings me in the cuticle. The bee isn't angry. It didn't realize it would die with that action. It just did.

The truck's dashboard clock says 6:20 PM and we still have another couple of hours before the day's end. We need to move one more yard of nucs from the forest because lumberjacks will come tomorrow to cut it down. Single deep hives line the road and three of us lift them onto the truck bed it slowly moves forward. My knee is swollen fat and my back aches. I'm hungry and ran out of water an hour ago. But when I stop for a moment and take in the scene in front of me—the truck, my co-workers, the trees, the dirt road, the flying bees, the setting sun, the fading heat of evening, the bright forest scent—I feel completely happy. I would take this over a commute in New Jersey any day.

We ride for hours together in the truck. Three of us sit shoulder-to-shoulder in the cab while another lies in the sleeper behind the seats. We talk about how tired we are, how much longer we have to work, how unfair the bosses are. We argue over the radio station, we take turns choosing it. We work together in the field, we rely on each other, we finish each other's jobs to make the day shorter. We let out fragments of our hopes and desires, but not enough to show any vulnerability. We make jokes about sex. We make gay jokes. We make animal

sex jokes. We make gay animal sex jokes. We are all sex-starved. On the rare night we aren't too tired, we go to the RAF in Oberon. We drink beer and play pool. We talk with each other. We don't speak with any girls.

There is a wallet-sized drawing of Jesus taped to the wall above my bed. Next to it is a vial of water. I assume it is holy water. I left the drawing and vial there to see what would happen.

Hundreds of millions of people around the world have a job like this. Manual labor, harvesting, scratching dirt for a few vegetables, factory work, sewing, making cheap plastic crap. Everything that you see right now was made somewhere. Whoever made it came to work every day, did the same task again and again, then went home with meager pay.

They complained about their bosses and scraped by with the hope that one day their children would not have to live the same life, or do the same kind of work.

The kookaburra is an amazing bird. His boisterous laughter melts everything else away. Sometimes I hear them from afar, many of them laughing at the same time, and a warm glow grows inside me. I also really like the local wild parrots. They flap about and gather together for a good squawk. The drama I hear is real, like bickering old women in the treetops.

I keep a notebook where I write down stray thoughts, quotes, ideas, memories, so they don't flutter away. Flipping through it I see one quote:

Pause you who read this, and think for a moment of the long chain of iron or gold, of thorns or flowers, that would never have bound you, but for the formation of the first link on one memorable day.

—Dickens, *Great Expectations*

I do think for a moment. New Zealand was a long time ago, I conclude, and I had no idea it would lead me here. A few pages later I come upon another quote:

There is only really one serious philosophical question, which is whether to commit suicide.

—Camus

"You're not the guy I need right now, Camus," I say. Then I go to the living room and join Lauro in front of *Deal or No Deal.*

While at Rose's house for a BBQ, we watch the video of her mother's funeral. Warren tells us that at the age of 101, at the breakfast table one morning, Rose's mother announced she wasn't going to be around much longer. A few minutes later, she died.

The video had many long takes of family members dressed in white shirts standing next to the body, blinking, with dramatic music invoking Jesus in the background. The body was in the house for two weeks before they walked alongside the hearse ten kilometers in the blazing sun to the graveyard.

It is the first funeral video I have seen, and I am fascinated. From my seat on the couch I can see a frozen pig's head in the sink. Later we will feast on an amazing variety of spiced, Filipino food, and I have been promised all my karaoke dreams will come true.

I have a bad day. I'm fed up with the spiders. I grab a broom and go on a mass killing spree, hitting all the corners I can find, mashing them against the ceiling and wall. Afterwards I see the fresh stains of spider bodies and realize where the old stains had come from.

The following morning the spiders and webs are there again. Those living in the hidden corners must have been waiting for this opportunity and have moved out to fill the prime spots.

The car doors slam, and the engine noise disappears down the road. I am alone. I walk around the house, surveying my domain. It's much better now, after a big clean by Neneth and I, but there's still grime to be found at every turn. I look at the floor, some kind of plastic, maybe linoleum, but more fragile, with the printed texture of wood. It's a confusing series of squares inside of squares, interlocking, folding in on themselves, locking in an increasingly smaller pattern.

Why am I looking at the floor? I open a bottle of wine, pour a glass, and sit down. The wine has AC/DC, a rock band, on the label. Why does AC/DC make a wine? Why did I buy it? I take a sip. It isn't good. The empty house is oppressive. I think about going for a walk, but rain starts to fall. It's Christmas Eve in Black Springs.

I should be somewhere else.

28

Thailand Temple

2013

"Phu Phan?" The pudgy hotel clerk repeated my words, incredulous. "Phu Phan!" I doubled down, pointing in my notebook where I had painstakingly copied the Thai script from Google Translate. The clerk chuckled and said something to a fellow worker. If either of them spoke English, I would have said, "As I was researching bees and beekeeping in Thailand, I saw a photo of a giant tree which was home to over a hundred nests of *Apis dorsata*—the giant Asian honey bee species that live on open comb and migrate long distances. The article accompanying the photo was only a paragraph long and stated that the tree was on the property of a monastery in Phu Phan, which is in an extremely rural area just east of Sakon Nakhon. Have you heard of the monastery? And how can I get there?"

Leaving the hotel and starting towards Sakon Nakhon's bus station, I had a sinking feeling that I might have underestimated my task. Phu Phan was not a town, I realized, but a district. Also, by the way I was turning people's heads, I could tell that this was not an area accustomed to tourists, and it would be tough to have a more informative conversation than the one I just had. Other than the Thai script for "Phu Phan," I had also written down words for *honey, bee, honey bee, bus,* and *monastery*. It might be a long day, I thought to myself.

Near the bus station I found street cart selling Thai iced coffee—one part espresso, one part condensed milk, two parts ice poured into a plastic bag and drunk with a straw—a dessert for breakfast. With this sugared boot to the brain my spirits bounced back and I walked into the bus station as if I knew what I was doing. The local buses—trucks with a few seats nailed to the back—were not much like the buses I was used to, and it took a handful of awkward questions before I was directed to one bright blue truck half-full of waiting passengers.

I have spent a notable amount of time in bus stations during my travels. Though all have that same whiff of impermanence, they are also places where cultural and philosophical differences are laid bare. In America a bus has a timetable: you know when the bus will leave (or at least when it is supposed to), where it will go, and you know it will follow this schedule even if you are the only one on the bus.

Elsewhere in the world, in rural Thailand for example, a different frame of mind prevails. When you find the correct bus, you may be thankful that to see it is only half-full and you jump in. Then you wait. There is no timetable. The bus will leave when it is full. Depending on the popularity of the route, departure could be anywhere from fifteen minutes to two hours. For someone with a schedule-driven frame of mind, who has been raised in a society where time and money step hand in hand, this can be infuriating. It is difficult to overcome this

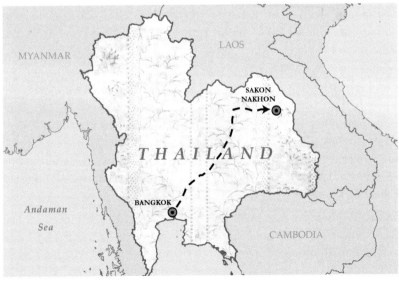

emotion. You start looking at every person walking near the van, hoping this one will get in, maddened if he doesn't. You form a customer-arrival rate in your head and bake it into a time schedule. As the bus gets close to full, the driver might switch on the engine as an enticement to other potential passengers, and the truck's diesel fumes join the others that have been mixing in your lungs.

I learned that it was better to emulate the locals, to whom a ticking clock instills no fear. They resign themselves to the idea that an arrival tomorrow would be as fine as an arrival today. Glaze the eyes and gaze afar. Let the body sag. Buy another soda from a bus station hawker and throw yourself to the wind. Learn how to wait.

The Phu Phan bus—if I was, indeed, on it—was semi-popular on this weekday morning, and a steady trickle of people climbed into the seats. When an old grandmother wrapped in colorful clothes filled the final vacancy, someone dragged the driver from the cafe, and the old, bright blue truck rumbled into life. With a heavy belch of diesel smoke, we lurched into traffic and soon were on a country road outside of town.

The coffee buzz began to fade and left me rationally thinking about my predicament: this bus was moving, and I didn't know exactly where I wanted to go. Phu Phan was a county and included a national park of the same name. All I knew about the monastery was that it had a bee tree. I looked at the faces of my fellow passengers—Thais of all ages and shapes—with more than a few looking curiously back at me. Sizing each of them for the best advisor, I chose a well-dressed woman across from me.

She didn't speak English, but the girl next to her knew a few words. I showed them my notebook with scratched Thai bee-words. To my surprise, she seemed to understand me and signaled I should wait. Fifteen minutes of steep road later, she said something to the driver and we pulled into a small turnout. The girl pointed at a dirt road leading to a clearing in the forest. I thanked her, climbed out, and the bus sped away. I was alone. Small sounds of the tropical woodland filled the air. This was it.

I walked down the dirt road, my eyes searching the canopy for a bee tree. Soon I began to hear human sounds and in the clearing I came across a medium-sized temple under construction. Maybe six people were building a large wooden mold for pouring concrete, while four others seemed intent on erecting an iron-pole tent. An impressively life-like statue of a meditating monk sat under a canopy just far enough away that I had a niggling thought that maybe it wasn't a statue. There was no bee tree in sight. I stopped in the shade to weigh my options. Soon one of the workers approached me and I gave him my notebook spiel.

"Dong Champoo Wat," he said definitively and gestured to a nearby motorbike.

"Great!" I said and asked with gestures, "How far?"

He held up three fingers. Three kilometers. "Great!" I said again. He yelled something to his co-workers, I climbed behind him on the motorbike, and we drove, somewhat surprisingly, back onto the main road.

Houses dotted the jungle and the road passed quickly. We skirted at least one pothole that would have caused us both grave bodily harm if struck at speed. It wasn't long before he slowed suddenly and turned into a grass driveway. With skepticism growing, I dismounted and looked at the place. It seemed to be an abandoned mid-range hotel. Unsure of the custom, I offered the guy a few bhat, which he took and drove off. Soon a woman opened the door of the hotel and approached me. With her hair in a gray bob and a warm smile, she looked like the Thai version of my 8th grade English teacher. She was quite friendly, and deeply wanted to help me, but my spiel didn't go very far with her.

"Dong Champoo Wat," I finally said, and that lit her up. She pointed down the road.

How far, I gestured, and she held up three fingers. Three kilometers. I thanked her and began walking.

The sun was high and the roadside dusty. The place wasn't exactly a village, but more like a road with houses along it along with a few quiet, side businesses just in case tourists decided to come this way. A tiny restaurant with a hand-painted sign. A deteriorating wooden stand with soft drinks and candy. It was not a pleasant day for walking. I soon took a long-sleeved shirt out of my backpack and made a makeshift turban against the sun. Unlike the Thai people who never seemed to sweat in any amount of heat, my body began to turn on the waterworks.

In a few minutes I approached a house where a guy was dozing next to a stack of watermelons. The watermelon is the ultimate combination of drink and food: safer than the local tap water, more satisfying than soda, and the perfect snack on a hot day. I bought a small melon, sat on a shaded, dusty log and consumed the entire thing. The guy's family, who had come out of the house to watch me, tried to hide their chuckles.

It's at this point I should say that I was wearing a pair of white-and-blue-striped overalls which I had recently purchased at a covered market in Bangkok. I then had a Thai tailor cut them off at the knees, making them into an untraditional pair of train-conductor-overall-shorts. Beneath this I had a Transformers t-shirt. Some months later, when wearing this same outfit around friends, I was chided for looking like a giant five-year-old. Add this outfit to your mental image of a giant, western guy walking along the roads of rural Thailand with a makeshift turban and a notebook of vaguely-scratched symbols while searching for something uncertain and a bit crazy.

With my sticky hands held into the air, the watermelon farmer pointed at a nearby spigot where I washed my hands. Feeling much better, I gave them a thank you thumbs up, and then continued down the road. A hundred paces later I came upon an auto shop where a young guy worked under the open hood of a car. He was my next victim for the notebook spiel. Mid-way through it, a car pulled over and the driver shouted something out the window. The mechanic answered and brought my notebook to him. A conversation ensued, and eventually the driver signaled for me to get in the backseat of the car.

"Why not?" I thought.

There was a driver and passenger, both Thai, and the passenger spoke some English.

"We go to Wat," he told me

"How far?"

"Few kilometers."

I wanted to ask if it was three, but I refrained.

Outside the landscape soon became uninhabited, and I was thankful I hadn't continued on foot. We turned off the main road, descended into

a valley and eventually drove into a swampy clearing peppered with houses standing on eight-foot stilts. The driver, peering out his open window, spied a monk sitting on one of the porches and signaled him over. The monk, in the traditional orange robes and carrying a lit cigarette, approached the car, soon revealing a variety of bad-ass snake and thorn tattoos across his chest and arms.

Another discussion ensued. Apparently this settlement was Dong Champoo Wat, and there was no such bee tree here. The monk had an idea and gave the driver some more directions. They thanked him and we drove away, turning out of the compound and continuing along the valley.

My drivers were a sort of Thai-flavored Cheech and Chong. Loud and a little faded, they talked and laughed a lot with each other, and sometimes involved me in the conversation though I had no inkling of what was going on. The passenger—Chong—was in charge of the music and would eject each tape after half a song, rifling through the shoe box of tapes at his feet for the next. All tapes were a form of screechy Thai singing. By this point I realized wherever we were going was not on their way, but they seemed to be the kind of guys who had free time and would enjoy whatever direction they traveled.

We turned once, turned again, and soon came into a hot, hilly forest. Three kilometers had passed around twelve kilometers ago. Finally we took a hard right, and the car struggled to carry the three of us and itself up a narrow, paved road along a ridgeline. At the top I saw a majestic temple hidden among the trees and vines. With massive pillars of worn stone, it seemed to be pulled straight from an Indiana Jones quest. My excitement built: this was as deep into an unknown world as I had ever been. These monks sequestered themselves in the far-flung jungle to live the simple life, free themselves from the trappings of modernity, and get in communion with a deeper spirit. I, braving the hot climes, language barrier, and poor transport, was the bold explorer who battled his way here. I was already forming the story in my head, one I could tell at hostels and family events to come, of what life was like in the ultimate other, and how I got there.

The three of us got out of the car and walked towards the temple. Soon I heard a booming voice and when I came through the temple's stone entrance I saw an elderly monk sitting cross-legged on a pillow atop the steps, elevated above a group of silent children—young monks with shaved heads, dressed in orange, their lives stretching out simple and profound in this place. When the monk spied me, he stopped talking and all heads turned. The entire journey swelled into this moment—my notebook, my spiel, my bee words: what was I supposed to say in front of this entire group of people? But before I could act, the monk asked "May I help you?" in perfect English.

I should have known by then that most monks speak English. It frequently happened that, while wandering a Thai temple, a monk would approach me and start a conversation. This was part of their English practice—speaking with foreigners—and I was always happy to oblige.

The revelations only continued as my adrenaline faded. I soon saw that this temple—the Indiana Jones one—was fairly modern, with power outlets, light fixtures and a sink that could have come from IKEA. Upon the brief interruption of their ceremony, some of the adult monks on the edges brought out their cell phones and began texting. In fact, these kids, far from the life-long Spartans I had imagined, were actually here at a summer camp. It was a monk summer camp. I was invited to join their final "novices" ceremony," which involved a long speech from the elder monk and a few group chants. Soon a pile of mothers and fathers showed up to pick up their little monklets. The scene was not too different from my own times of being picked up after a week of summer camp.

With the ceremony over, the elderly monk and I spoke for a while. He knew both English and Italian, and was originally from Bangkok but came to this place twenty years earlier because he "liked the breeze." We talked about bees, which he knew more than the average person, but he was not a beekeeper because monks do not believe in disturbing animals.

"All these children will be very wise," I said, gesturing at the kids who were currently getting fawned over by their parents.

"I don't know." He seemed skeptical. "Maybe."

Most importantly, he told me I had found the right place. The bee tree I had been searching for was a few hundred yards away. The monk had some parents to placate, so he left me with a man who was the mayor of a nearby town. I got on the back of the mayor's motor bike and we coasted back down the ridge line into the clearing where the tree stood.

It was a massive tree. Its spiny, leafless fingers stretched against the blue sky, the thicker branches flecked with dozens of *A. dorsata* nests. *A. dorsata* doesn't live in a cavity like the European *A. mellifera* because southeast Asia never has a winter; *A. dorsata* is able to build a single, giant comb attached to a tree limb for the whole world to see. The base of the tree was surrounded by a six-foot wide and tall heap of barbed wire to prevent honey hunters from attacking the nests. As I looked up at the tree, what the monk had told me a few minutes earlier was confirmed: all nests were empty. *A. dorsata* is a migratory species—though no winter, there are seasons of dearth and the bees migrate across the country to find different food sources. I had come at the end of the dry season and the bees would be back in a few months.

"Cool!" I said aloud. The mayor watched me, leaning against his bike. I picked up an old piece of comb that had fallen off the tree. It was as big as a pizza. What else does one do in Thailand? Get drunk on a beach? Visit temple after temple?

"Cool!" I said again and took a few pictures. Was this it? Had I traveled to this region of the country—of the world—and spent the entire, ridiculous day in order to pass five minutes saying "Cool!" at this giant bee tree with no bees in it? I guess so. I guess that's exactly what I had done.

I asked the mayor to take a picture of me with the tree and the comb, but after that there was nothing to do but leave. I climbed back of the motorbike and the mayor drove me ten minutes to a gas station. Almost immediately I found a truck which would take me to Sakon Nakhon.

In the back of the truck, I rode shoulder to shoulder with a few other passengers. With wind whipping away the sounds, a one-toothed old man and I traded a few hand signals, but we didn't get much past the pleasantries. As we were descending the hill back to Sakon Nakhon, I saw a road sign for a waterfall. I still had a few hours before sundown and banged on the back of the cab. The truck dropped me off on the side of the road and I was once again left with the small sounds of the tropical forest. I walked past the boarded-up welcome hut and followed the trail into the woods. After ten minutes I came into the clearing with the feeling that something was amiss. I didn't hear any water. Ahead of me, the riverbed was dry. I looked at the rock formations for a few minutes, but then sat down on a nearby bench.

A beeless bee tree. A waterless waterfall. It wasn't my day.

29

China Pollination

2013

"If the bee disappears from the surface of the Earth, man would have no more than four years left to live"

—Einstein(?)

This quote circulated through the media a few years ago, and its simplicity and sensation caused it to stick in many minds. I am sometimes assaulted by it after telling people I'm a beekeeper. My response is usually this: this concept is not based on fact; Einstein was a physicist, not an entomologist, and this quote surfaced without reliable citation sometime in the 1990s. A good *Apis* spokesperson can debunk this myth (as well as the problematic statistic that one-third of our food supply is pollinated by bees), while in the same breath also strengthen the case for the world's need for honey bees. While perhaps not responsible for something as melodramatic as the survival of humanity, the honey bees do vastly improve our quality of life.

"Money makes the world go round," might be the more appropriate quote to use when speaking of the commercial pollination of our foodstuffs. It's easy to see this in the American beekeeper-grower relationship and it's no less evident in the Sichuan province of China, where for the past twenty years pollinating fruit trees by hand has become standard practice. When Colony Collapse Disorder and the fear of bee extinction emerged in the mid-2000s, this region of China began to be noticed by the world's media. Journalists and news outlets already had images of beekeepers in the vast California almond orchards—the flawed present—but with a pesticide-drenched land in China where all the bees had died and the farmers were forced to undertake intensive, human labor to produce fruit, the documentarians then had a perfect dystopian future to point to.

In actuality, like the pseudo-Einstein quote above, hand pollination in China isn't quite as straight-forward as it is portrayed. My goal while traveling through China was to write a series of articles for the *ABJ*, and this issue of hand pollination was on the top of my list. After a few cold calls, I finally got in contact with Dr. Ya Tang, an ecologist based at the University of Sichuan. When I came to his office he sat me down and asked me what I knew. "Not much," I said. Then he told me, "Hand pollination in Sichuan is 100% an economic issue."

Dr. Tang had a bone to pick with some journalists about this subject. He had recently been interviewed for a documentary, and though he speaks perfect English, the filmmakers asked him to give his answers in Chinese. When he saw the film, he was shocked that they did not translate his words correctly into English—they downplayed the economic issue for their anti-pesticide push. His agreement to meet with me was a hope that this story could be corrected.

Maoxian county in Sichuan is one of the biggest pear and apple producing regions in the world. Hand pollination of fruit is practiced here, but this is common throughout China. In other parts of Asia, farmers still don't understand the concept of pollination, but the Chinese are well aware of its significance in producing a proper yield. Orchard owners collect and process the pollen themselves then hire laborers to dust the flowers using feathers attached to a long bamboo pole. Pollination must be accomplished within five days of blossoming, and one person can pollinate five to ten trees each day, depending on the size of the trees.

But why not let bees do the work? Firstly, farmland has increased to the detriment of natural habitat, reducing the amount and variety of forage for native pollinators and wild bees, especially in the lower, more populated valleys. Secondly, the apple orchards do not have enough pollinizers—trees that provide viable and compatible pollen—to allow adequate cross-pollination. It is recommended that 25-33% of trees in an orchard need to be pollinizers to ensure a satisfactory crop, but in Maoxian county most orchards are small, from twenty to one hundred trees, and the farmers don't want to waste their land on pollinizers which do not produce fruit. Thirdly, the area has suffered through four decades of intensive pesticide sprays with farmers dousing their tree between eight and ten times per season. Agricultural extension work for fruit growers is rare and most orchardists are uneducated about the negative effects of pesticide use. When they rely on a crop like apples for their livelihood, they would rather overspray to ensure their success. This practice has both discouraged beekeepers from putting their bees near orchards and been harmful to the native pollinators. The local government once tried to reintroduce beekeeping to the area, but the beekeepers ended up losing many colonies due to heavy pesticide use and were not compensated.

The practice of hand pollination began in the late 1980s. Though it required much more labor, the farmers found hand-pollinated trees produced more fruit, even causing tree branches to buckle under the weight. The practice hit its peak in the 1990s but then began to decline in the 2000s due to the drastic socioeconomic forces that began to change the entire nation.

A 2001 survey showed that 100% of the apples in Maoxian were hand pollinated and the farmers paid workers only ~$2 per person per day. With apples at a relatively high price in this period, this practice was economically feasible. But the following years saw a decrease in apple prices and the construction boom began to draw people towards lucrative jobs in the city. In a few short years the surplus of rural labor dwindled to almost none. In 2011 farmers paid human pollinators $12-19 a day, wages much too high for the price of the apples. Instead, the Maoxian farmers have replaced the apple trees with plums, walnuts, loquats, and vegetables; crops which do not require pollination and bring in much more profit. Currently, plums are the main fruit tree present in Maoxian, and apple trees only exist where farmers are unable to find suitable alternative options or if they live near forested areas. While agriculture is extensive lower in the valley, more natural vegetation is preserved higher in the mountains where pollinators are

abundant. The beekeepers of the area also spend their time in higher altitudes, away from the pesticide use.

But as the price of apples has decreased, so has the excessive spraying, as the apples are not worth the cost of the chemicals. This has allowed both native pollinators and honey bees to make a slight recovery. Extension work in the area is still limited because the Chinese government is not concerned with "cash crops" like fruit trees. They don't want to invest time and money in these crops when the whim of consumer taste will change in a few years. Instead the Chinese government focuses its research and extension work on cereal crops. Even for Dr. Tang, who is an ecologist, this Maoxian situation is a side project from his main research of improving the efficacy of growing sorghum and other grains used in a popular kind of Chinese liquor. I guess liquor will always fall within the whim of consumer taste.

Though the season for fruit tree pollination had passed, I still wanted to see the area for myself. From Chengdu I took a bus to Wenchuan, the regional capital and the focal point of the hugely destructive earthquake of 2008, which leveled the city and killed tens of thousands of people. By the time I visited in 2013, the city was built anew and looking fresh from the giant injection of money it had received from the government. I found an inexpensive room and spent a few days walking around the place, eating food from small stalls, climbing the surrounding hillsides, watching people gather for a coordinated dance in the main square every evening.

I spent another day in Maoxian, where the documentarians usually filmed hand pollination. As in Wenchuan, the city curled itself along the river, with fruit farms spreading up the steep hillsides. While walking through surrounding villages and looking at the fruit trees, I thought of the shifting economic and ecological forces at play. They were tied together with the same paper green as can be found in the almond fields of California. When the price of almonds drops, or a cheaper and more effective pollination option appears, even a powerful quote or moving voiceover won't be able to turn the tide. The economic engine only takes one kind of gas.

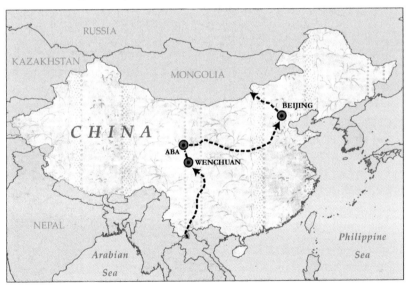

30

China Bus

2013

❦

"**H**ONGYUAN!" I shouted again. The woman behind the glass replied by saying something in Chinese, and I felt the ten people in line behind me take a step closer. In China, the social contract of line-forming does not hold much, if any, weight. Often it needs to be physically enforced. At most train and bus stations, the lead-up to the ticket counter is a set of metal fences which look like a third world border crossing. These barriers funnel each line towards a teller without allowing the possibility of anyone jumping ahead. Without this infrastructure, a mass of human flesh would be pressed against the counter, money held in balled fists, all inching towards that opening which would dispense a ticket and get them out of there.

I could hear the frustration behind me when I said the name of the town once again, pronouncing it slightly differently, trying to say it as I imagined a Chinese person would. A travel guide in front of me showed a simple map of the province. I wanted to head to the north through a remote, mountainous region, a not-well-traveled one, but I couldn't pronounce the name of the town which would be my first stop. I tried showing her the map, but it didn't have Chinese characters. Despair was creeping in. It was 5:40 AM.

"OK." I looked at the map again. "How about ABA?" Her face twitched in recognition. She scratched something on a ticket and handed it to me. Aba was another town in the area, not exactly where I wanted to go, but it was what I could pronounce. I didn't know anything about either place, so Aba seemed like it would work just as well as a stop heading north.

The town of Wenchuan was dead quiet at this hour, or I should qualify that by saying it was quiet outside of 25 yards around the bus station. With this perimeter, it could be mistaken for a county fair on a hot Friday night. It seemed like every family farm in town sent someone to hawk fruit to those traveling elsewhere. After buying a bag of cherries I must have looked lost enough that a tiny older woman wearing a pious blue robe over some hip Nike sneakers guided me to the correct departure spot. Soon, a bus appeared, and my fellow travelers and I, each carrying a bag of fruit, boarded and found our seats. The bus rolled out of the parking lot, across the river, and took the left fork up another valley. With responsibility out of my hands for the next eight hours, I took the opportunity to catch some lost sleep. The motion of the bus snaking along a winding road rocked my dozing head back and forth between the window glass and my fellow passenger.

When I woke, the sun had risen, the river had transformed into a hard-running stream, and we had entered a new clime; shrubs replaced the trees and the spring flowers were still in bloom. Soon I caught sight of my first beekeeper: a variety of jars and bottles set up on a wooden table, a beat-up truck next to a burlap tent, and the beekeeper enjoying his morning tea while watching about sixty hives head out to find their breakfast.

This scene repeated itself a few more times, and I rued the fact that I couldn't ask the bus driver to pull over so I could meet the beekeeper, taste the honey, and buy a few jars. Then, the bus did pull over at a small hut, and as I looked for the nearby hives, two policemen climbed on board. Without a pause they pointed at me, the only Westerner on the bus, and signaled that I should follow them. The suddenness of it shocked me, the flip from gentle bee thoughts to law enforcement, and I was still arranging my head and squeezing the knot in my stomach when they brought me into the police hut on the side of the road and closed the door.

The knot was in my stomach for a few reasons. Firstly because of visa issues: getting a Chinese visa is not straightforward, especially if it is an American trying to enter from a foreign country at the last minute. I was traveling overland from Malaysia to Mongolia without a set schedule, and China was a major part of that route. For an American to get a thirty-day Chinese tourist visa, I needed to submit evidence that I had a plane ticket both in and out of China, as well as a schedule of hotels where I would stay each night. For my traveling style, this was akin to going to a museum wearing a straight-jacket and a blindfold. But I had a plan to get around this. Directly before submitting my visa application at the Chinese consulate in Vientiane, Laos, I bought a round-trip plane ticket from Hong Kong to Kunming that was fully refundable for twenty-four hours. Then I reserved five nights at six different hotels throughout China. Right after handing in the application with these receipts, I canceled them all. A few days later the visa was approved, and I had my first test of the system when I crossed into China on the Laotian land border. When the bored border guard stamped me in with little fanfare, it confirmed my belief that the country was too big and too messy for them to care about a slight gaming of the tourist visa. But on the side of the road, when the police man picked up the phone and began calling someone with my passport information, I began to feel the snaking tentacles of deceit creeping up my legs, my hips, and my chest.

"Where you go?" the policeman asked me.

"Aba," I replied.

With his English and my Chinese, that was about the extent we could communicate. After a short conversation over the phone and a long inspection of my passport, he handed it back to me and pointed at the bus. Relief swept in. When I boarded, I waved sorry at everyone for the extra minutes of waiting and stepped back to my seat. The bus ground its gears and continued climbing. I felt happy and relieved to leave the incident behind me.

Not twenty minutes passed before déjà vu struck: the bus pulled over, two policemen climbed aboard, pointed at me, and I followed them to the hut.

"Where go?"

"Aba." One officer picked up the phone, the other snapped a few photos of my passport, and my stomach twisted itself again. The second reason for the knot was that though I didn't really consider myself a journalist, my main goal in China was to research and write a series of articles about the country's apiculture industry for the *American Bee Journal*—hard to not call that journalism, which I was pretty sure needed a different type of visa. I had emailed many beekeepers and scientists across China asking for information or if we could meet, and someone could have easily passed my emails and questions to some authority. Add to this that China was in the midst of a massive honey adulteration and smuggling crisis, and you could say it was a semi-sensitive issue. Finally, and not the least worrisome, China has a poor reputation of jailing journalists. Again, I didn't think I was a journalist, but it would be a bit of a tough sell if someone turned the microscope on my intentions.

These thoughts raced through my head, along with a more composed one which said I was overreacting, and there was nothing to worry about. After the officer got all he needed to know from the other side of the line, the déjà vu loop completed with my passport handed back to me, getting back on the bus, sheepishly waving to the other passengers, and letting our group once again continue forward.

Not again, I thought to myself when the bus pulled over at the next hut. But apparently it was Groundhog Day, and this scene repeated every twenty to thirty minutes: the police pointing at only me, I getting off the bus, into the hut, and the same, "Where you go?" and sometimes, "Why you go?"

"I hear it's very beautiful," was my stock answer. At one point an officer had to ask someone on the phone about the word "passport" which was written on the front of my passport. "Passss-port" he said clearly, three times, to the party on the other side of the line. By the fifth or sixth stop, my nervousness had worn away and was replaced with impatience. In fact, I began to feel cocky, waiting in the hut, practically tapping my foot as they made another phone call to Chengdu or Beijing or wherever to get instructions about this foreigner. "Don't you guys talk with the others down the hill?" I asked one officer, who didn't understand me. I also began to feel bad for my fellow bus passengers as I had personally caused them over a half-hour of delay to their journey.

189

But no feeling could distort more quickly than when, on the 7th checkpoint, the policeman yelled something at the driver, who got out of his seat, opened the underside of the bus, and dragged my backpack onto the ground before getting back in and driving away. There I was, on the side of the road on a barren, harsh plain, in the hands of a few Chinese policemen who spoke fragmented English, who were unable to tell me why I wasn't allowed to continue or what would happen to me. Suddenly every minute of my future, from the next moments to my far-off goals, was stamped with an unforgiving question mark.

I sat on my bag, taking it all in. The landscape was like North Dakota or Bolivia or Mongolia—wide, uninterrupted, and not a place where you want to be caught outside when a storm strikes. Soon a police car appeared, and they wedged me in the middle of the backseat between two officers. We drove ten minutes to a dusty collection of squat, brick buildings, one of which appeared to be a police station. A gang of bored policemen hung around in front of it; one officer was busy washing his hair in an outside sink. Intensely aware of the whereabouts of my passport, I watched two officers take it into one part of the building, another officer pick up my bag, while a third led me through a doorway covered by a hanging blanket into a room which only had a hard wooden bench. The room had windows, but they were boarded up, and when the officer dropped the blanket I was left with an internal twilight, the sharp line of light from the bottom of the door a contrast to the dim pall that sat over the rest of the room. I was flooded with the deepest loneliness of my life: in a sunless cold room on the high plains of China, without a passport, without anyone I could call, at the mercy of whichever bureaucrats were currently sifting through the fallacies of my data.

It was a long time before one policeman pulled the curtain back and stepped inside.

"I'm sorry," I said.

"Where go?"

"Aba."

"No Aba," he replied.

I thought a moment. "Hongyuan?" He nodded. I continued: "Hongyuan, then Lanzhou, then Beijing."

He said something in Chinese then stepped out again. In a few minutes, he pulled back the blanket door and signaled me to step out.

The gang of police officers still hung around outside, and I immediately spotted my bag next to one and my passport held by another. Almost all were smoking cigarettes. One guy said something and everyone laughed. Another picked up my bag and carried it out to the road. I sucked in all of these visual signs, and every piece of body language, trying to glean what would happen.

I only knew I would be OK when they began talking about the Celtics. They, as a group, were trying to deduce where in the US I was from and when I said Boston they immediately began talking about Ray Allan, Kevin Garnett and other basketball names I vaguely knew—the same basic conversation I had gone through dozens of times on buses and trains with the many Chinese NBA fans. I gave these officers a lot of thumbs up because that was my main conversation tool, and because the worry inside me began to melt. The man who I deduced was the most senior office found a piece of paper and, using my passport underneath as a writing surface, drew a crude map of directions on it—Hongyuan to Lanzhou (the next big city to the north) with the major towns between. Soon the officer with my bag shouted, and an incoming bus pulled to the side of the road. The policeman drawing the map didn't change his pace; he leisurely continued plotting my route all the way to Beijing while the other officers and I kept naming NBA players, and the bus idled.

When the map was finished, we walked together to the bus, like old friends seeing me off. I could feel the escape, and I couldn't resist the question. "Can I take a picture?" I pointed at my new NBA-fan-police-officer pals.

"Bu" the senior office said sternly, and I put away my camera. The bus was nearly empty and I sat in the very back seat. As the bus pulled away, the gang of policemen waved. I waved back, then laid down on the seats and curled up in a small ball.

It wasn't much longer before I learned more about the situation. Aba—the town I didn't want to go to but was the only one I could pronounce—had been the site of riots at a very sensitive time before the

2008 Beijing Olympics, when Tibetan monks had attacked government buildings, torched a dozen cars, and where both civilians and
police had been killed. The town was still, in 2013, essentially closed
to foreigners. The other thing I didn't realize about my haphazard
itinerary was though I wasn't technically in Tibet (going there is very
difficult for foreigners and something I knew not to try), a large region
of the Sichuan province is on the Tibetan plateau. It docsn't require
the same special permission to visit as the province of Tibet, but it is
still well-populated with Tibetan people and suffers through the same
issues of overrule, oppression and resentment. Hence all the check-
points.

I learned this from a Tibetan man, who I will call Tenzin, who acted
as my translator at the next checkpoint on my bus journey (yes, there
were a few more), and who tipped me into an unexpected and highly
interesting stay in Hongyuan. After helping with the police, Tenzin
invited me to eat at his restaurant later that evening, and I arrived
to find a family meeting in process. I ate a delicious yak-meat stew
as Tenzin's small children gaped at me, shocked that I didn't know
Chinese. Tenzin became a touchstone for me around town as I found
myself thrust into the troubles of the Tibetan people. Over my three-
day visit, I drank at least a dozen yak-milk teas with kind and generous
Tibetans who wanted to tell me their stories, or ask me about what was
going on in the world, because at that moment they had no access to
the internet. Though many western websites are blocked throughout
China, this area had its internet completely blocked, phones included.
Exceptions to this rule included government buildings and the police
station. This meant that all their news came from pro-government
propaganda TV and radio.

The police, who were not Tibetan and had a heavy presence around
town, were greatly feared. Whenever I entered a restaurant, the owner
would peek out the door and then close the curtains so passing authorities couldn't see inside. Then I would hear tragic stories, like how
the young woman with a heart-meltingly warm smile who just served
me tea had just come out of her five-year prison sentence for illegally
broadcasting the Voice of America radio program to other people in
the region. Or how my host, Tenzin, who was a teacher, had also just
finished a two-year stint in jail for teaching certain "Tibetan facts" to

his middle school class. Now he was free and building a tourist hotel in traditional Tibetan housing, but without the Internet to connect him with tourists this business would prove improbable.

This is why you are here, Tenzin told me. The Chinese only want tourists to stay in the proper tourist hotels, to take pictures of the Terracotta Army, the Great Wall, or the Forbidden City of Beijing, and leave thinking, "This is China." They don't want tourists traveling on their own, talking to people, and learning about what is really going on inside the country.

He spoke the truth that was running through my veins when I canceled all the hotels while applying for a visa. The next day, while hiking in the countryside outside of Hongyuan, a Tibetan man appeared in the door of a hut and ushered me inside. His English was very basic and we could share only a limited amount of information, but he was so excited to meet me that I felt like an old friend. He gave me a tea and, oddly, an ice cream bar, and then asked if he could take a picture of me with his horse. As I stood holding the reins of the old horse, the grassy Tibetan steppe behind me, I thought to myself: yes. This is why I am here.

31

China Impostor

2013

The city of Beijing has seven ring roads. Seven. The first is very small, only ten miles long and surrounds the very core of the city—Tiananmen Square, the Forbidden Palace and so on. The past decades have seen this metropolis spill beyond its bounds again and again, swallowing up surrounding towns and villages to create a massive urban mess blanketed with smog from the multitude of illegal and unregulated factories operating within. The seventh ring road is five hundred miles long: nearly a full day's drive. My guide picks me up at a subway station somewhere between the third and fourth ring, and we drive to the northeast. I hope that after clearing the final ring we will see some sun, and I'll catch a glimpse of the Great Wall. But it doesn't, and I can't.

After an hour's drive, we arrive at the Jingchun Beekeeping Cooperative. The smog is less here but everything is still the monotone gray of a dystopian future. After I stretch my legs and get my bearings, a highly polished, jet-black car pulls into the parking lot and two people emerge. One is the president of Beijing Beekeeper's Association and I immediately realize they are taking my "bee journalist" mantle a lot more seriously than I am. This guy is no beekeeper moonlighting as a club president; he is a politician who somehow squirmed into the field of beekeeping and climbed to the highest possible rung. He is wearing a pair of fancy slacks, a tight dress shirt, and shoes that match the shine of his car. Looking down at myself, I see stained and torn clothing that I had already worn for three consecutive days—one of three outfits I have carried for the past seven months while living out of my backpack. However, even with his exquisitely up-combed coiffure, I am still about eight inches taller than the president.

Within thirty seconds of shaking hands, we begin taking pictures on the steps in front of the cooperative. First, three different people are taking pictures of the president and I, then the coop's main beekeeper joins us, then I step out and photograph the president and my guide and the student, and so on until nearly all combinations of people are captured (including a pleasing photo of the just the president's driver and myself), until we finally gather for the group picture. As with every picture of when I am near the president, he moves upwards a step so we are almost, but not quite, the same height.

We are in a room on the second floor of the beekeeping building, sitting at a long conference table. Green tea is served. "What would you like to know?" my guide asks me. I realize I probably should have prepared more for this meeting, but getting in the car that morning I didn't exactly know where we were going or who I would meet—information that had been lost in translation. I am supposed to be a journalist, I keep telling myself, and all these people are here because of me. I start asking about honey production, honey quality, pollination, extension work, apitherapy, and whatever follow-up threads pop up in my mind. Every question goes through my translator to the president, and then comes back as a well-polished answer. I'd like to know more about the most interesting topics that dog Chinese beekeeping—adulteration of honey and use of illegal antibiotics—but every time I poke at these subjects I am assured that their honey is very clean, is constantly tested, and they have no such problems in Beijing. As I scribble down my notes, Mr. President watches me with a patient smile. Outside there is a frightening crack of thunder, and rain begins pelting down.

The rainstorm dissipates as quickly as it appears, and we head back outdoors for another photoshoot. First we take more pictures together in front of a billboard showing a computer generated graphic of a giant museum and visitor center that will be built on this location. The ground has already been broken, though further construction doesn't seem readily apparent. I can easily envision Mr. President posing here with a hardhat and shovel.

Almost on cue, Main Beekeeper hands Mr. President a hive tool and a pith helmet, and he pops open a nearby hive. The bees are surprisingly docile. Instead of a donning a veil or lighting a smoker, a smoldering cigarette hangs from Mr. President's bottom lip. He takes out a frame and motions for me to come over. We inspect the comb together and I nod along as he explains to me in Chinese. Others take pictures of us as if he is showing me some great truth about brood, larva and Chinese bees. He is completely in his element in front of a camera. Bees buzz around us, but surprisingly no one is stung.

Suddenly the sun appears. It might be the first sunshine I have seen in a week. We get in the cars and drive a few minutes to the top of a hill where a marvelous view of a forest and a reservoir lay below us. This is the water supply for Beijing, the president tells me, so there is no industrial pollution here, and it is possible to make very clean honey. Under the glow of his "trust me" smile, the sudden appearance of sunshine seems a little too good to be true.

Twenty minutes later everyone is sitting around a table with their glasses raised. We are in the private room of a restaurant, with the glass windows facing a view similar to the hilltop. "A toast," my guide tells me, and together we drink a dose of baijiu—a popular Chinese hard liquor made from sorghum. But it doesn't stop there. Next my guide toasts me personally; he thanks me for coming to China and my willingness to try new things. We drink another shot together. It is rude to not drink on a toast, I had been told. Next his student toasts me. The glasses are filled: to my pursuit of bees and beekeeping. The glasses are empty. A waiter places two more full bottles of baijiu on the table—I see we are drinking an expensive brand. The toasting moves around the table, much like the photography, so every personal combination is achieved; my guide toasts the president, the president toasts the student, the student toasts the president's driver who shakes his finger—no, no—and holds up his glass of water. But I, as the guest of honor, seem to be on the receiving end more than average, and the liquor is quickly going to my limbs and head. Faces around the table are turning red. Laughter is looser and louder. The president toasts me again—"Full glass!" he shouts in English, as I try to only sip the top of my shot, and I am forced to bottoms-up.

A score of waiters enter the room and place steaming dishes on the enormous glass Lazy Susan—three feet in diameter—that is the center of the table. I don't recognize much of the food but take a plop of each as they spun around the table, anxious to have something to balance out the baijiu sloshing around my stomach. The guide whispers in my ear—"It is extremely rude if you don't toast the president." Though another drink at this moment would deeply threaten to crack my internal inebriation gauge, I also fear the cultural stumble and wave my glass at a nearby waiter, who cracks open another bottle. I stand up and say something about the quality of beekeeping and the president's commitment to the beekeepers and then a few more sentences until I realize I don't know exactly what I am saying anymore, but it doesn't matter because only my guide can understand, and he gives a concise translation before the president and I drink, full glass.

Next two waiters carry in a plate with an enormous fish—three feet long—and they place it directly in front of me. My guide tells me it is from the reservoir below us and was probably more than ten years old. The driver takes on the carving duties. He cuts off the cheek—the best part of the fish, they tell me—and holds it over my plate.

"Take picture," he says.

I am wasted. Completely. We are somewhere else now. After lunch, where toasting sporadically continued through dessert, we climbed into our vehicles, drove to another beekeeping center and had another meeting on another long table in a concrete building. They served another green tea, which may very well have saved my life, and I ostensibly had a discussion with Mr. President and the person in charge of this facility, but most of the time I was grappling with the fact that I was somehow born in my body on the opposite side of the world instead of being born here in this obscure corner of China. Mr. Guide is translating my questions and then translating back their answers. I am scribbling down words, most of it illegible. I need some air.

Then we are outside watching a few men pick through giant plastic panels stacked on the ground. Each panel is about six feet tall and six feet wide, and two of them together make a sign the size of a billboard. There is much fuss about finding two panels that match, and they need to flip through the entire knee-high stack which, at the moment, I find quite entertaining. Finally they find a corresponding trio and stand behind it, fitting them together to create a picture of a honey bee pollinating a flower with a sentence in Chinese beneath it. I have no idea what this is for, though they may have explained it to me inside, and I am afraid to ask again. I need a nap. Everyone is here because of me. We take another group photo.

We are at another restaurant. It hasn't been more than two hours since we finished the last meal, but over the course of this meal and others the previous week, I am beginning to understand the subtle wining-and-dining culture that is a part of Chinese business—every nice restaurant had a multitude of private back rooms where one party seemed to be catering to another. Somehow I've mixed myself in this swirl, and we are back in Beijing city for round two. This time the centerpiece of the table is a hot metal dome surrounded by a moat of broth. Slices of raw meat spin around the Lazy Susan, and the custom is to slap the meat onto the hot piece of iron to cook it for a few minutes. Of course this is all complimented by bottles of baijiu. The recent dip back into sobriety foretold a glum future, and I prepare to climb that mountain again. I raise my full glass and thank the president for a wonderfully informative day and tell him he's a great man, but to my utter surprise, he picks up his water in return. I am trying to process this when the driver takes his own glass of baijiu and toasts me back, full glass. The president, who had been so gregarious the entire day, is suddenly focused on his food while the driver, who is completely fresh from his day of drinking water, picks up the banner and begins sparring with me. I, in my advanced state, am a willing combatant, and the driver and I keep toasting each other, back and forth, back and forth, at some point switching to beer. The meat spits hot juices down the iron dome and into the moat broth. The Lazy Susan spins around. I take a bite of rice. I take a bite of meat. I take a bite of salad.

Maybe that salad was a mistake, I think to myself thirty minutes later while riding the subway. Chinese guidebooks state that tap water is dangerous and one should only eat cooked vegetables and drink bottled water—raw salads might be washed, but might not be completely dry. The concept of hidden droplets on lettuce is floating about my woozy, drunk head when the slight tickle in my stomach suddenly and shockingly ratchets ten-fold to a throbbing railroad spike. In one moment I am vaguely wondering where I will find a toilet on the way home, and in the next I am in a dire, dire emergency, so I stand up to disembark at the next station, wherever it was in the city. Everything in my body is clenched in a horrible way as I stumble out of the car and look around for anything resembling a restroom. None are in sight, so I head for the exit which turns into an endless escalator to the street, five stories high, and I only make it half-way before realizing there is no hope. It all comes out.

Everything. A wet, smelly, relief dribbling down both my pant-legs, into my shoes and onto the metal steps of the escalator. This is the worst moment of my life, I think to myself. One can definitely have worse moments, but this moment is mine, take it or leave it. Someone is a few stairs behind me on the escalator and I can't bear to turn around and face that undoubtedly horrified individual. The second half of the escalator ride is agonizingly long, and at the top I walk straight into a small grove of bushes and lie down. My head is on wood chips, and my brain is pickled in baijiu. I lie there for a long time. The sun has set, and the city is dark. Through the branches I watch the red and white lights of a busy road swim from top to bottom of my vision. Quietly, to myself, I sing the song, "What if God was One of Us?"

Time passes. I'm really not sure how much. Eventually the moment arrives when my brain convinces me that inertia is not a viable long-term option. No genie will whisk me away. Action must be taken for survival. And so I sit up. I consider all the possible routes towards so-briety and cleanliness. I have very little idea where I am in relation to my hostel and have no phone or map. I do have an address and cash. No amount of money would be too much to deliver me there. I climb out of the bushes, back into the vertical world. Mouthing the deepest apologies to the driver, I hail down the first cab I see.

32

Italy Providence

2013

I was close. Terribly close. Yet at that hour, under the cold, florescent lights, it all seemed lost. The plan had been moving seamlessly that afternoon, but my luck sank with the sun, and I was now stuck at a gas station on the Swiss-Italian border. People shook their head at my English words and dropped their eyes as they walked inside to pay. The door opened, the door closed: another rejection. My own engine, running on adrenaline and hope, sucked at the final drops—it had been thirty hours since I climbed out of bed. Tiredness greedily filled up every void. From my slumped backpack I took out another layer—my rain jacket, though it wasn't raining—and put it on for warmth. Standing next to the ice machine all night wasn't an option, but I didn't have a back up plan. I really needed a friend or a savior to finish the day.

It had began in my childhood bed in Massachusetts. After packing and a farewell lunch, my mother drove me on the winding road east where we got stuck in Boston traffic, and then I was alone and stuck at the check-in counter, stuck in airport security, and stuck in a tiny airplane seat for 10 sleepless, wine-tinged hours until I was dumped into a chilly-but-beautiful early April Swiss afternoon.

Flights have always been the pillars of my travel plans; normally booked months in advanced, they stretched the canvas while, in between, I traveled with the improvised arc of the brush. Today was no exception. My destination was Slovenia via Padova, Italy, where a few friends were playing a concert that Saturday. I landed in Zürich on Thursday. I could spend the weekend with my friends in Padova and then catch a ride back to Slovenia. The timing and logistics seemed perfect.

To get from Zürich to Padova meant heading one hundred seventy-five miles south through the Alps, then taking a dogleg in Milan for another one hundred fifty miles east along the northern Italian plains. Before my flight I had looked at train tickets and was shocked at the prices; the cost was not much less than another plane ride across the Atlantic. A bit more sleuthing showed that it was the first half of the journey, the Swiss part, which racked up the cost, while the slow train from Milan to Padova would only put me back around $20. Even though I was landing in the afternoon after a long flight, the solution was immediately obvious; I would hitchhike to Milan and, from there, take the slow train to Padova.

The plan started out better than expected. A bus took me from the Zürich airport into the city and set me down near a highway sign which pointed towards Milan. Half the battle of hitchhiking is finding the right spot to catch a ride. In rural areas the process is straightforward: find a pull-off at the edge of town and stick out your thumb. In a city this can get much more complicated, especially in an unfamiliar one. It can take hours of inquiring, walking, or bussing to discover a corner where vehicles aren't driving too fast and are also potentially going to your destination. With that battle over (you hope), the next step, waiting for a car to acknowledge your thumb, can take another few hours. On this day luck was shining: the airport bus dropped me off in a good spot, and it was less than twenty minutes before I saw the brake lights of a Fiat pulling onto the shoulder, and I was whisked out of the city.

Milan and Zürich are major cities, and I had hoped to catch a traveler going the entire distance. Instead my rides were short, lasting ten to forty minutes, though they were amicable and came steadily: a semi-professional soccer player on the way to visit his family, a car salesman on a business trip, a diehard windsurfer in a van replete with his boards and stories about the different, deep lakes that we drove past.

The border grew closer; signs began to have text in both German and Italian. If I could make it to Milan that night, I thought, I could crash on the couch of a friend of a friend, and then take the train to Padova the following day. I waited at a roundabout at the northern edge of a town and soon a tiny Piaggo slowed and stopped in the middle of the road. The guy inside didn't speak English, but we somehow figured each other out: he wasn't going very far but could drive me to the other side of town where I would have a better chance at getting a ride south. He was, I could tell, a fellow traveling spirit, and he clasped my hand firmly before he drove away. Waiting at this next roundabout, I looked at the sharp mountains surrounding the small Swiss-Italian town. Though the sun was setting, the future skies looked bright.

A camper van soon pulled over, and I climbed in. The man, a kind of missionary, was not heading to Milan but would bump me another ten miles down the road. During the ride he covered a lot of ground, telling me stories about fearing for his life in tiny African villages while spreading the word of God. He probed at my feelings towards the Almighty, but I didn't give a green light. He wasn't offended, and before dropping me off at a gas station he offered to buy me a sandwich or a coffee, thinking I must be hard up to be traveling this way.

I declined his offer, suddenly realizing the odd juxtaposition of my day—from Swiss Air to Swiss dirt. In the deepening dusk, I put on another layer of clothing and walked to the well-lit awning. This was a highway gas station—forest on one side, highway on the other, cars stopping to fill up their tanks and move on. I was less than a mile from the Italian border. One more ride and I would be within reach of Milan's public transportation, and then I could find my way across the city towards a friendly couch.

For a while I stood on the road that led back to the highway, but the cars kept sliding by. Trying to flag a ride from the side of the road at night is an unwelcome chore; imaginations darken with the sky and drivers only feel suspicion at the brief flash of a haggard figure standing next to a backpack. Perhaps rightly so. After some time, I moved back to the lights of the gas station and stood next to the sliding door where I put on my best puppy dog face. As each driver parked, I wondered if they would be the one to get me out of there. As they pumped gas, I thought of what I could say that would convince them I only need another few miles.

The rejections continued. No one was going into Milan, or no one trusted a vagabond soliciting rides at this hour. My eyes were only open due to adrenaline, but they weren't going to be open much longer. My pillow from this morning was only a vague memory now. What a long way I was from there.

When the point of overflow struck, I picked up my bag and walked around the gas station. In the back I followed a service lane, ducked under a gate and came upon an empty country road. I could go right, uphill into darkness, or I could go left, downhill into darkness. I chose left. Without sun, the air had a sharp chill, but the sky was clear, and I had a sleeping bag. I walked only a minute before turning onto a small dirt track. Where could I crash? The shadows of trees leaned in on me and I could no longer see the lights of the gas station. Fear, the rational kind, was in check, but irrationally poked against my breast. It wasn't every day that I had to find a spot to hunker down on the Swiss-Italian border.

I forged on.

Soon a glade opened, and a row of stomach-high dark shapes appeared. My eyes were getting accustomed to the darkness, but I still couldn't quite make out what these odd shapes were. I reached out, and when I touched the wood and metal, I immediately knew.

Beehives. A few dozen of them lined up on a frame. I laughed. Hitchhiking is a pursuit that makes you realize that the corridors of life are endless. Every car that passes is a ride to a different existence: one could be driven by a generous king, another by a serial killer. Each ride will set you down in a different spot and expose you to a different geography and a different set of drivers, one of whom will take you off to another singular splinter. Though life is always like this, hitchhiking exposes the hall of mirrors to me and resets the thoughts in my head. Though I don't believe in fate, I treasured moments like this, where instead of being thrust into an unknown megacity well beyond my element, somehow the path led me here, to a group of beehives in the woods, where I belonged.

I pressed my ear against one hive and knocked on the wood. I heard a sleepy buzz, but no bees wanted to brave the cold night air. I took out my sleeping bag, pulled off my boots and slipped inside. Reaching up, I could still touch one of the hives, and I was reminded of that other night, so long ago, when I slept next to the packages in my car in New Mexico. Through the clearing in the branches above me I could see a few stars. Strange cracks and swishes came from the surrounding forest—night sounds from animal drama unknown to me. No matter. I was safe here.

The following morning, I woke up early and found the bees already flying. I watched them for ten minutes as my mind gained traction and I centered myself for the coming day. I had slept well, no night creatures caused me harm, and the peacefulness of waking in nature was an unexpected joy. After packing my things and saying goodbye to the bees, who were already bringing in pollen, I walked back to the gas station. Standing next to the ice machine with a rested brain, bright morning sun, and a steaming cup of coffee in my hand, I felt a million miles from the night before. The first guy that passed told me to get in his car and we drove not just to Milan, but half-way to Padova. He had a business meeting to attend along the way, and instead of dropping me off, he told me to wait for him in the lobby and after he would drive me to the nearest train station. In the presence of a stylish Italian secretary who had on earrings the size of dessert plates, I whiled away an hour with cappuccinos and Samuel Beckett before the guy returned and we continued east. My driver was a designer of heating and air filtration systems for indoor aqua parks. I was a beekeeper and honey bee researcher. We asked each other a million questions about our respective careers, each thinking: people do the strangest things.

33

Morocco Guest

2014

I've had many emails ignored during my traveling career. When visiting different countries, I often reached out to local beekeepers or researchers hoping to connect with someone and find something to write about. If I didn't know anyone through my network, I would look on the internet and start cold-contacting people. The reply rate wasn't high, and the successful reply was even lower. I understood: people had busy lives and did not want or have time to entertain a foreign stranger. Yet as I made these calls, always in the back of my mind I had the dream of the perfect host. This archetype came to fruition in Morocco, in the guise of Khalid.

Khalid implored me to visit him in El Jadida, a small city on the coast of Morocco. I had just come from a bee conference in Murcia, Spain, had ferried across the Strait of Gibraltar, and spent a week travelling south from Tangier. My wanderings had led me to a small town in Morocco's central mountains where a Berber marriage festival was underway: nomads gathered from all over the country for a weekend of matchmaking and speed dating. In a dusty two-computer internet café, within earshot of bleating sheep at the livestock market, I found Khalid's enthusiastic email in my inbox. Though El Jadida was a few hundred miles out of my way, his excitement for a visit was enough to give up the last day of the festival and push further south.

I arrived in El Jadida at nightfall. When Khalid picked me up at the bus station I was surprised how young he was—in his mid-twenties, with a short crop of hair, olive eyes, and an easy smile. He drove me to a hotel, which I had to stop him from paying for, and instead of dropping me off for the night, he brought me to his honey store on the other side of town where he seemed to have an ongoing bull-session with his friends. We drank tea, tasted his variety of honeys, and laughed at pranks they played on each other. By 2 AM, when he brought me back to the hotel, I already felt like I was part of the crew.

Khalid and I then spent three days together discussing all things bee and beekeeping in Morocco. As gregarious as the definition, he was constantly on the phone: checking in, plotting, laughing. He had two phones, one of which was broken so that whenever someone called he had to pull out a flashlight to see the name on the screen. I was delighted by this oddity of character in him, like him eating a packet of mayonnaise in a moment of hunger. I was also impressed by his bee skills: Khalid was a breeder of *Apis mellifera sahariensis*, a rare, native desert subspecies of honey bee. He also specialized in harvesting daghmous honey, made only in minuscule amounts (around a ki-

logram per hive) from a desert cactus in the arid south. Upon tasting daghmous honey I noted a delectable sweetness, but then my mouth oddly began to heat up like the sensation of rubbing Bengay on a joint.

One afternoon we drove an hour south to have a cup of mint tea (or three) with a beekeeper, and Khalid acted as translator for all my questions. The next morning we traveled to a small patch of eucalyptus trees surrounded by a thousand hives on the barren desert: a convincing display of the oversaturation of the country's beekeeping industry. In the evening we visited one of Khalid's friend's and ate a traditional tajine, the best meal of my year, and I rode the crest of a high that was my goal for every traveling experience: the taste of foreign culture and connection over boundaries that can't be bought with money. It made all the cramped, long bus rides, and dingy, overcrowded hostels worthwhile. Also, after being constantly assaulted by hawkers and fake friendship in the city of Tangiers the week before, it was a wholesome relief to find that the fabled Moroccan hospitality was in truth.

Upon parting, Khalid gave me two things: a small jar of daghmous honey and a big jar of homemade amlou, which is a thick, heavenly paste made from almonds, argon oil, and honey that we had been

eating all week. Then we got in his truck and started towards the bus station.

My mind was elsewhere while we were driving, but I knew we had time before my departure and I still needed some presents to bring home. I asked Khalid if we could stop at El Jadida's central market to buy some more amlou. He looked back at me, exasperated.

"Why didn't you tell me you wanted more?"

"No... but, don't give me more, I want to buy some. For my family."

He mumbled something in Arabic to his friend in the passenger seat, and I sucked on my teeth, wondering if I had made a cultural faux pas. Khalid circled back to his store, ran inside, and brought out another jar, once again waving off any payment I tried to give him.

At the station, Khalid slapped palms with the guard and then drove me inside the terminal, dropping me off a few feet from my bus. I was heading to Marrakesh where I had a few more days before my flight back to Spain. Getting onto the bus, I felt the weight of transition—no longer an honored guest, I was once again fumbling in a foreign country on my own. I found an empty seat and waved goodbye from the

window. Khalid, sitting on the hood of his truck, had already run into someone else he knew and was working on his next scheme.

At the end of the first day in Marrakesh, I began to face the dilemma that had been seeded when Khalid gave me his gifts: how would I bring the honey on the airplane?

I stumbled into one of these problems very early in the game—when I flew from the US in September 2006 there was no ban of liquids on planes, but when I flew back in December of the same year, policies had changed unbeknownst to me and two bottles of top-notch wine were snatched from my carry-on at the Paris airport (they had allowed them on the first flight from South Africa to Paris, but on the second leg to the US they were barred. I implored the French customs agents to take them home, but the regulations stated the bottles needed to go into the bin).

On my Moroccan trip I only had a small carry-on bag. As delicious as they were, I wondered if two jars of amlou and one jar of exquisite honey was worth a $75 checked bag. I began this debate on my final night,

211

and the question wasn't settled by morning. Instead of spending my final hours exploring the sights of Marrakesh, I continued looking for a solution to this problem. I bought a cardboard box and some tape, then found the postal office and stood at the back of the line. It was a long line, maybe two dozen customers, with seven of them crammed up at the counter trying to be next (as in China, line civility was not a thing here). For as long as I stood there, perhaps thirty minutes, not one customer moved forward. I'm not sure if the top customer was a dire case, or if the postal workers were on an extended morning break, but nothing happened. Though behind me the line grew and dissipated, everyone ahead seemed jaw-set to wait it out. I watched an old wall clock slowly tick towards my hour of departure, and when it was no longer feasible to make it to the teller in time, I gave up. Holding my carry-on in one hand, the cardboard box in the other, backing through the post office's door required an awkward shove of my hip, and the jolting motion sent the box from my hands and crashing to the stone floor.

With the dull thud of glass, I knew the game was up. Everyone in the building watched as I peeled open the box to inspect its contents. One jar of amlou had broken inside its plastic bag, the other amlou and honey were intact. Heartbroken and angry, I picked up the box and burst out the door. I briefly considered salvaging what I could of this precious paste, but the thought of swallowing microscopic glass shards made me look for the nearest trash can. The post office was in the city's main square, but no trash receptacle was within sight. In a fit of rage, I dumped the plastic bag in a large planter that might have once held a tree, but now only held dirt and cigarette butts. A lady passing by turned to me, aghast.

"Oh, you tourists think you can just litter here in our city..."

"No, I... No..." the explanation was too hard, words wouldn't come, and my anger needed a focal point anyway. "THERE ARE NO TRASH BINS HERE," I yelled, and she yelled back, and I yelled again, and she threatened to get the police on the other side of the square and I said some of the choicest words I could think of and stormed off, feeling a bit of release, but still carrying two jars of problem and finding myself nowhere closer to a solution.

My backup plan involved using the post office at Marrakesh's airport. When I arrived, the desk behind the window was empty, and it took a long search through the terminal to find the teller on her extended coffee break. She told me that this post office only sold stamps and did not take packages.

My options had dried up. I stood in the flight check-in line, accepting the lost cash and cursing the airport security. Then the situation then amplified when I reached the counter and discovered that the price of a checked bag doubled to $150 when purchased at the airport. When questioning the woman behind the flight counter about this, she said to me, "Why don't you just ask someone else to carry it in their luggage for you?"

It must be sound advice, I thought, if I heard it from the airline worker. I looked at the people in the check-in line behind me.

"Sorry, can I ask you a question? Look, I'm a beekeeper and I like honey. I have been visiting beekeepers here in Morocco, and one gave me this really nice and expensive honey, but I can't bring it on the plane. I know this sounds weird, but would you pack this in your bag for me? Just until we get to Spain? It's really honey, I'm not a terrorist or anything, here, taste it."

Alas, it seems we are past the innocent days where one would help a beekeeping stranger in trouble at the airport. After my second rejection I realized the folly of this pitch, and I retreated with tail between my legs. I soon found myself seated across from a trash can which would suck away the physical and delicious remnants of my beautiful visit.

My flight was boarding soon but I wasn't ready to give in. Looking at the trash can wasn't inspiring, so I did a lap around the terminal. The plan came to me as I watched a worker meticulously stack a pile of plush stuffed camels in the airport's souvenir store. I had to try, I thought. With Khalid's generosity and his second trip back to the honey shop to get another jar of amlou, there was no way that I could not try. And so, I made my way to the airport's bathroom.

Inside the toilet stall, I put down the seat and sat down. I found every plastic bag I had in my backpack, dumped out their contents, and prepared them for their payload. At first I tried to be careful, but there was no hope of neatness about the process. I had no spoon or utensil, so I scraped the bottoms of the jars with my fingers. This honey, I reminded myself as I licked my fingers clean, cost around $60 a kilo. The taste was exquisite, and I enjoyed every particle, though my mouth grew quite hot, not in a spicy way, but with a different sensation altogether. I double-bagged the honey and then moved onto the amlou, which was chunkier and didn't flow easily from the jar. In normal circumstances I would have savored both of these riches, stringing them out in tiny tastes over weeks and months, but here in the Moroccan airport bathroom I loaded what I could into cheap plastic bags and sucked down whatever was left. In a nearby stall, someone let go an unceremonious fart.

The amlou butter, I decided, could go in the carry-on bag, since its state as a liquid was more debatable, especially when it was no longer in a jar. The honey, however, I strapped against my inner ankle which was then covered by sock and boot. As I was standing in line for airport security, I tried to play it calm, but the thought kept running through my head: is this what a drug mule feels like? It was not a particularly good sensation, hiding a secret from authorities, and I felt the honey squish against my ankle with every step as I passed through security machines and under the gaze of the uniformed men and women.

214

Thankfully, the Moroccan security was not overly thorough. They waved me through the metal detector without fanfare, and my bag went through the scanner without a second look. Once on the airplane I settled in my seat knowing that I had not failed Khalid's generosity, and my two gems from Morocco would make it back with me. Given the circumstances of their packing, however, I decided that the honey and amlou might no longer be considered proper-quality gift material, and with a not-too-heavy heart, accepted that I would have to consume them all myself.

34

Nigerian Decision

2015

Beekeeping has the intriguing potential to be a tool in the fight against dire poverty. Keeping bees doesn't require land ownership, hives can be built out of scrap materials, and swarms can be captured in the wild. With a bit of education, people with few resources can acquire an interesting and useful skill. Those who are often at the bottom of the social or fiscal ladder—women, children and the elderly—are able to empower themselves with a modest means of support. Years before, I had spent two summers working on a community-based conservation project in Kenya, the fruits of which later became the backbone of my college thesis. It wasn't long into my beekeeping experience before I began reading about developmental beekeeping schemes in Africa and Asia, and realized the possibility of taking the work I had done in college and combining it with honey bees.

Over the years I had a few near-misses—either the timing or funding for the project hadn't worked out—but in the fresh months of 2015 a chance appeared. Winrock is a company involved in a variety of agricultural projects around the world—from shrimp production in Bangladesh to small-scale duck rearing in Turkmenistan—that also frequently posts beekeeping projects. Often these kind of projects focus on marketing or improvement of honey production, which I didn't have much experience in, but this project fit my profile well: two weeks of "training the trainers" in queen breeding, disease management and the production of organic honey. The timing was good, too. I had decided to move to Slovenia but was currently in the middle of a three-month wait as bureaucracy processed my work permit. With growing excitement, I wrote an application to Winrock, endured a phone interview, and a few days later received an email inviting me to Umuebe Farms and Farm College in southern Nigeria.

The email came just as I was just starting a two-week cross-country trip from Montana to Massachusetts by bus and train. My days were busy with irregular and exciting events—demolishing an old house in Missoula with Austin, a friend I'd worked with on a bear study in Montana, ice fishing in sub-zero temperatures in Northern Minnesota with my moonshine-distilling-lawyer friend Richard, and marveling at the seeds of growth coming from the wreckage of Detroit with Deana and Chris, a pair of budding mushroom entrepreneurs. Yet all along the way, the reality of my upcoming trip kept poking its head back into my business, and I wondered if there was always this much news from Nigeria, or if I was just noticing it more because my flight was approaching. The country's presidential election would occur a few days before I arrived, and Winrock had warned me that if any political violence flared (as had happened in the previous election), they would delay sending me. Also, Boko Haram, an extremist group known for their extra-extremeness, seemed to be expanding their attacks from the northeastern borderlands into the rest of the country.

On previous trips I had gone to countries that were not known to be overly safe, and to some countries that had earned travel warnings from the US State Department. My poor parents, though they worried, had been supportive of my adventuring. Despite this stream of bad news from Nigeria, I was committed to this trip because of the skills and opportunity I could offer. When my cross-country journey finished and I was back at my parent's house in Massachusetts ten days before my flight, I finally sat down to plan out the lessons and logistics of the project.

At my desk I found a sheet of paper and scribbled at the top: Day 1. I had two weeks to train the trainers. Start from the beginning, I thought. In Umuebe Farms' introductory letter they wrote about their Langstroth hives and Jenter Queen rearing kit. I looked at the splash

217

of white on the paper and began painting it with everything I knew about queen breeding. But something wasn't adding up. What could I teach these Nigerian beekeepers that would be useful? And what about their bees? West Africa is home to the honey bee subspecies *Apis mellifera adansonii*, which is renowned for its defensiveness and tendency to abscond—when the entire colony leaving their hive at a minimal disturbance. I put the piece of paper aside and began clicking around the Internet to find something in support of this project.

Days passed. The logistics of the trip began to solidify. My Nigerian visa was approved and my plane ticket had arrived. Winrock sent me steady guidance on the nature of volunteering, and the host coordinated my arrival. While this was going on, I continued researching queen breeding and *A. m. adansonii*, tying together thoughts that had been floating in my mind like dark clouds appearing over a mountain range. Finally, with enough information and a solid opinion, I voiced my concern to Winrock: I didn't this like project, breeding queens in West Africa, was not feasible.

Winrock said they would still like for me to go: regardless of the feasibility, the beekeeper at this school wanted to learn about queen breeding and they had agreed to provide him with a resource. They connected me with a few previous volunteers to assuage my concern. The first contact gave me a quick and optimistic answer: you should just go, be flexible, and even if the project is flawed something will work out. This response was familiar. It was advice that fit my traveling mindset and could have easily come from my own lips.

Another former volunteer, Ann, provided a more detailed and complex answer. Ann was a well-experienced beekeeping volunteer and teacher in her sixties. She had been to Nigeria with Winrock a handful of times and could immediately see where this project came from, where it would go, and why it wouldn't work. Beekeepers in Nigeria (and elsewhere in Africa) read about massive European beehives, bumper honey crops, and bees you can handle without wearing gloves. African subspecies of bee live in small colonies that yielded only a fraction of the honey and attacked in drastic numbers. ("Bring rubber dish gloves and duct tape," Ann told me, "and if attacked by the bees, run through the vegetation to try and lose them.") After a disturbance, a hive of *adansonii* can stay defensive for hours, even days, or the disturbed colony will sometimes just pick up and leave. How can one work in a hive, much less stock a nuc, if the bees will just abscond?

"Queen breeding is not the answer," Ann told me. Most likely the Nigerian beekeepers didn't have a full understanding of bee biology, as in they didn't know that the two dozen drones who mated with the queen came from any hive in the area. You could select an egg from the gentlest and most productive hive, but even if it was possible to raise a cell without the hive absconding, you would have no control over the male genetics and essentially are back to square one.

What about organic honey? I asked. How can they know what is going on in the thousands of acres around them, or from what ministry do they get a certificate? Ann countered. Disease management? Ask them if they can identify what diseases or pests they have, Ann told me, or if their knowledge of diseases and how to manage them is another something picked up from the Internet.

I read these words with a sinking heart, knowing that I should have seen these obstacles and fallacies long before I applied for a volunteer position. I had been sun-blinded by optimism, trust in the aid organization, and the opportunity of subsidized travel to a foreign land. This is the sad story of so many well-intentioned aid projects: people with good hearts and ample funding try to help the less fortunate in a foreign land but merely stumble into something they don't know much about and waste resources along the way.

Ann had other advice to offer: what the Nigerian beekeepers do need is to fully understand is how to work with their bees and their climate. Beekeeping with *A. m. adansonii* and *A. m. scutellata* (the East African subspecies with similar temperament) is truly left-alone-beekeeping. Maintaining good equipment and understanding the weather patterns (dry and wet seasons, instead of summer and winter) as well as the variety of nectar flows are the keys to improving their situation. This foreign concept of queen breeding is understandable but misguided. Ann wrote that I should not assume that a concept as simple as "putting a super on during a honey flow and taking it off when it's done" is fully understood. On her previous volunteer trips, she had planned on starting somewhere in the middle, but at times had to backtrack and start from the beginning. It required seeing what equipment the people had and what they knew, and starting the plan from there.

Ann's advice swirled around in my head as the days paced forward towards my flight. My girlfriend in Slovenia wrote supportive emails which also held an undercurrent of worry. Then one morning I heard something on the radio which made me stop the coffee and turn up the volume: an American missionary in Nigeria, a schoolteacher in her sixties, had been kidnapped. Her captors climbed over the school's wall, fired shots in the air, and "whisked her away." She was being held for $300,000 ransom.

Kidnapping is not unusual in Nigeria. It is a business. The types of kidnapping varied: it could be a political action (like the extremist group Boko Haram which stole over 100 schoolgirls, most of whom haven't been found years later) or it could be for money. The kidnappers could be an organized gang, or they could be bored locals looking for pay dirt. Foreigners are not the only ones who are kidnapped—wealthy Nigerians are also in danger—but having white skin makes for a big target. With the Internet allowing news to bolt around the world, kidnappers can quickly command much power by capturing a foreigner.

Despite the kidnapping world news, Winrock told me the project was still on. Logically, this was understandable. They said they had a good host and took all possible precautions for my safety. Under their supervision, the chances of such an incident were very small. But it was hard for me to shake the bad scenarios out of my head. When living in Kenya for two summers I had spent time around people who were extremely poor. The majority of them were kind and took their situation with strength in a way that put my daily worries to shame. But desperation is a hard mother, and there were people who had been pushed to the edge who would jump at an illicit opportunity.

Then Ann gave me the best advice I could hear. She wrote, "I wouldn't go." When she had been to Nigeria years earlier the country had been fairly safe but watching the place over the years she had seen it growing steadily more out of control. "If you don't feel safe," she wrote, "then you shouldn't go."

It was what I needed to hear. I had not always been the safest traveler: I had ignored travel warnings, I had walked into slums, and I had slept on the street. But there was a fine line between going somewhere with potential danger and going somewhere with known danger. It takes a different kind of mindset for someone—a soldier, a journalist, an aid worker—to expose him or herself to danger in order to help others. And maybe this line was getting more distinct in my head as I reached a certain age. I was in my 30th year, I had a girlfriend I hoped to one day marry, and was about to move to Slovenia to start a stationary life. Perhaps a few years earlier I would have gotten on the plane just for the adventure, but age does a funny thing to the part of the brain that senses self-imperilment. In that moment it was pulsating: was it worthwhile for me to travel across the world just to tell these beekeepers that their idea was impossible?

No, I thought. It was not. My heart made the decision, but it took a full day of walking around the house before I could frame it in an email. I soon received a terse reply from Winrock stating their displeasure and reiterating that they already invested some $10,000 dollars in the project, which would be wasted if I didn't continue as planned. I understood Winrock's disappointment, and I apologized to them. I am sure that they are involved in good projects around the world. However, I argued that this was going to be a case of throwing away money and time, and that as an aid organization they should have a better understanding of the issues, or be more adept at weeding out such cases.

Sadly, this was not the first failed or futile project I have been involved in. These have all been disappointing, but one of the benefits of failure has been the ability to better recognize when another one was coming down the pipeline, and to re-boot and use the collective resources in a more productive way.

Another rock avoided. Perhaps it wasn't a rock at all. But the stream pushes on.

35

Slovenia Relations

2015

When the decision was finalized—the decision which ended my decade-long vagabond lifestyle and set me in Slovenia—and the proper visa paperwork finally came through, I rejoiced in the fact that I could start all the activities that required a stationary life. Getting a dog was on the top of my list, as was starting a garden and finding a comfortable kitchen with knives sharp enough to properly dice an onion. Another thing on my list to do this day was keeping my own bees. While I had opened thousands of hives and spent an untold number of hours reading and learning about bees, I had yet to have a hive under my own care. This was a big step. With no one above to give orders, there was also no one to blame but that guy looking back at you in the mirror (and no one to complain about, either).

I soon confronted the question of, "How?" Not only was I in unfamiliar territory in terms of the bee industry in Slovenia, but I also had the logistical snags of not having a car while living on the 6th floor of a building in the center of Ljubljana. And then there was the language. While all young Slovene urbanites could speak English ridiculously well, the beekeepers (old farmers, on the opposite side of the cultural spectrum) could not. I had moved to Slovenia in March. There wasn't much time to organize everything if I were to get bees that season.

Luckily I had the right people on my side. Slovenia has a special attitude towards the web of relationships cultivated through friends and family. If you have a serious toilet problem, you could call a random plumber in the phone book, but he might not come for a few weeks. It's better to call your brother's neighbor who will show up in an hour, fix your overflow, and then seal the deal with a shot of schnapps (and perhaps a hint that you can do a favor for him one day). In fact, one expression in Slovene for "terrible", or "inappropriate", or "bullshit" is *brez zveze*, which literally translated to "without connections". Without them, life in Slovene is a bumpier ride.

Kati, my girlfriend, and Meli, her mother, were both dentists. Many people sit in their chairs each day. Meli, in particular, was a formidable force when something needs to happen. She played no small part in muscling through the bureaucracy involved in my cross-Atlantic migration. So it wasn't too long after I started thinking about my bee-getting problem when she called to say one of her patient's brothers was the president of a nearby beekeeping association, as well as the mayor of a small town, and I had a meeting with him the following week. I was delighted. It was my first step towards spinning my own web of connections in this new homeland, and there was some hope I wouldn't have to continue with my brez zveze fumbling.

On the day of the meeting I was to borrow Kati's car and meet Miha, Kati's father and my translator, outside of the city. But my sense of time failed that morning (as did my alarm), and when I woke the clock face screamed that I was late. On the way out the door I grabbed a cold piece of pizza and some Easter candy for breakfast and then sped to meet Miha. Kati and I had been dating for a year or two, but this day was the first time Miha and I had spent time alone together. Miha—serious, business-oriented, extremely knowledgeable, generous—was a bit intimidating as a girlfriend's father, and I wanted to do everything I could to appear confident and trustworthy in his eyes. Thus, it was not a trivial ride over the hill as we chatted about bees, horses, Slovenia and whatever other topics drifted by.

Rain had drowned the previous night, but the temperature was dropping, and a transubstantial mix spit down upon us as we drove into the valley of Horjul. Agricultural fields surrounded the stream winding through the lower part of the valley while the village sat on the northern side with hills rising steeply in the background. On top of a prominent hill, looking down over everything, stood a large cross and a tiny church.

Miha drove into the village and we followed a sign for Čebelar (Bee-keeper). Slovenes typically live packed together in villages, where property is measured in square meters rather than acres, and from the balcony of the average house a person could probably hit six different neighbors with a tennis ball (or a rock if things are sour). Also, it is typical that every square meter of space is used, and the house we came to was no exception. A vegetable garden and a variety of fruit trees spanned from driveway to fence. Slightly uphill, next to the forest, stood a beautiful čebelnjak (bee-house).

The cellar door opened and we rushed out of the ugly weather. Inside I met the mayor and čebelar Janko. He had a strong white mustache, clear eyes, and a buzz of activity swirling about him. I shook his hand, tried my best Slovene greeting, and then put my hands into my pockets. There I felt something squish. Taking out my hand I realized the Easter candy had melted against my warm leg, and seeing melted chocolate on my fingers, my automatic reaction was to put them in my mouth. Then I caught Janko's eye, and a confused look at why I was sucking on my fingers right after we shook hands. Trying to recover, I put my hand back in the pocket, into the melted chocolate. Miha pushed past the awkwardness with the topic of the day. Too many odd layers to translate in the first 30 seconds of meeting, I thought. Best to let it pass by as another patch of intercultural weirdness.

As conversation between Miha and Janko continued, I excused myself and washed my hands in the nearby sink. At this point I looked around the cellar. On one wall hung multiple, large calendars showing plastic-looking, half-naked women handling a variety of power tools (a common sight in the automechanic shops and man-caves of Slovenia), while on the other wall stood a case displaying jars of honey and several framed gold and silver medals from honey competitions. Between these, on the tiled floor, lay bee equipment.

When I had the chance, I asked Janko my questions: where can I keep the bees? Where can I buy them? What were the blooms in the area? Soon, we got into his van and drove into the hills behind the town, the landscape turning a full winter-white when we climbed a hundred feet off the valley floor. At the top of the hills we reached an area of true beauty: steep cow pasture, forest and a farmhouse here and there. Janko brought us to a small patch of land between the road and a hollow where cows grazed. Chestnut and maple trees sat on the other side of the road. No agriculture or pesticides were nearby. I immediately began to imagine future summer evenings of watching the bees fly home, the dusk creeping down, and the night forest coming to life.

On our way down the hill Janko made a few calls, first to a beekeeper/blueberry farmer he knew in the town of Borovnica (Slovene for 'Blueberry') who would have swarms to sell that spring. Then he called an equipment dealer and ordered five hives. By the time we got back to his house everything was set, and I had the floating feeling of success. My odd dream, one I had been considering since my research scholarship in this country five years prior, had come to fruition: I was going to be a beekeeper in Slovenia.

After saying goodbye to Janko, Miha and I went to a restaurant where we continued our bonding over fried turkey steaks and beer. I was feeling pretty buoyant about the progress of life during the meal and as I drove back to the city. But reality came back when I parked, a few blocks from the apartment, and finally got a chance to examine the melted-chocolate-damage in my pocket. It wasn't too extensive, I had only grabbed a few chocolate eggs, but my house keys suffered the worst from their transformation and they needed a wash before use. Encountering a puddle on the sidewalk, I knelt down to rinse both the keys and my hands the water. A passing lady looked at me strangely, but at the moment I could see no better option. Then I continued to the apartment, where I dropped off my backpack, used the toilet, and then quickly left for a concert in the city.

Arriving home later that evening, I found Kati on the couch, looking a bit checkered. "Where are my car keys?" she asked me without any notation of it being a question, which should have been my first hint. I checked the counter where they normally live. I checked my pockets. I checked my backpack. "Umm..." I said.

What happened, we put together later, was that when I knelt by the puddle, the car keys had fallen out of my pocket. This puddle was in the center of the city, in an area frequented by junkies and shady characters. Instead of one of them finding the keys, then the car, and driving to a chop shop in Serbia, a woman spied them while walking her dog. She gave the keys to her husband who happened to be a police officer. Using the classic forgot-where-my-car-was-in-the-parking-garage key fob technique, he located the car a half-block away, looked at the registration and said "Huh, I think I know this family." Not only was he a policeman, but he had sold a big, black German shepherd to Miha a few years earlier.

Whatever trust and confidence I had built with Miha that afternoon crumbled beneath my feet, and I could only dream about that comfortable level I had taken for granted a mere day before. I cursed the chocolate for the mistake, though I knew it was mine alone, and I thanked the lucky gods for not spinning the day in a much worse direction. The roller coaster over, I stared at the ceiling that night, thinking of the hills above Horjul this summer, and the newest beekeeper in Slovenia.

36

Slovenia Secret

2015

It was early May in Slovenia and swarm season had begun. Swarming is when a honey bee colony—a super-organism—essentially procreates by splitting into two colonies. When a colony begins to feel too crowded for its current nest, the bees begin rearing a new queen. When the new queen hatches, the old queen will depart from the hive taking around half of its bees with her. This is the swirling, somewhat frightening storm of insects that you might see land on your neighbor's tree or disrupt a baseball game. In fact, while they are swarming, bees are mostly harmless. Honey bees use their sting as a defense—either in protecting their home or, in the case of being stepped on, their life—but since they are homeless during the swarm, they rarely sting. Instead they find a tree limb to gob onto for a few hours while scout bees flit about the land searching for a new place—a dry cavity about the size of a cooler, off the ground, facing south, at the edge of the woods—which they will call home. The newly-hatched queen, who in a few days will go on a series of mating flights, will then take over the duty of hive mother.

Swarm season is a good time of year to start beekeeping. Beekeepers who are negligent and do not take preventative measures find themselves with many colonies constructing and hiding queen cells on their combs. Once a colony tips over the decision to swarm, there is little, if anything, that can be done to stop it, so some beekeepers decide to let the swarm come (hindering the colony from making a honey harvest that year), but then capture the swarm and sell it. In my search for colonies I had been given a phone number of a beekeeper who was too busy with his blueberry patch in the early spring to deal with his bees, and he knew a number of swarms were on the horizon.

One evening I found a text on my phone telling me I could pick up two swarms the following day. It was time to get my first bees. The previous week had been an intense build-up—between regular work and other chores I had to paint hive bodies, assemble and wire frames, and attach wax foundation—but I had completed them all. The next morning I borrowed Kati's car, retrieved the bees, and drove back with two buzzing boxes—wooden sides, wire mesh top, about the size of a cat crate—seat-belted in the back seat.

We were living in a city apartment at the time, and thus my base of operations was Kati's parent's house. The offering of their garage as a workspace was the most recent link in their chain of generosity to me; they had already expended an inordinate amount of time and effort to keep me in Slovenia (with their daughter), and now they had helped organize the start of my Slovene beekeeping career by connecting me with Janko the Mayor and offering me this garage space.

Kati and Meli, a mother-daughter dental duo, have their clinic in the house where Kati grew up; the dental work happens on the ground floor while the family lives above it. I tried to imagine what it was like as a child living in such close proximity to a place of adolescent terror, but for her it seemed to be benign. At all points of the workday, six to eight cars were parked in front of their house, with nervous patients going in and numbed patients coming out in regular spurts.

I arrived at the clinic at around mid-day. It is best to put a swarm into its new hive near dusk. Sometimes, if the swarm is in distemper and doesn't like the shine of the new home, it will immediately take flight into a nearby tree, thinking it can do better than that rat-trap. A blocked hive entrance overnight discourages them from such a rash decision and by the morning they have usually lost their fire, making the best of what they were given.

Thus, I had a full afternoon to hold the swarms in their current state before they could start their new lives. I needed to keep them un-stressed in a cool, dark spot until the evening transfer. During this time, I also needed to feed and treat them for varroa mites. Parking Kati's car among those of the dental patients, my mind wandered around the property for the best location. Two outside storage closets stood out, but each had a downside: one held lawn-mowing equip-ment and smelled of gasoline, the other was a high-foot-traffic area next to the entrance of the clinic. Because the first had the potential for suffocating or poisoning the bees, I chose the second, waiting for a moment of patient inaction before shuttling the swarms into the closet and shoving them in among shovels and boxes. As I closed the door and went back to the garage, I felt a new weight hanging in my chest, one that any animal-owner or parent knows in one form or the other: that of responsibility. The potential disasters and deaths of my new charges blossomed in my head. I'd had the bees for less than an hour and I was already worried they wouldn't make it for any number of reasons.

The afternoon crept by as I worked in the garage. I had asked for five swarms and thus bought five Langstroth hives—the kind that is most commonly seen in America—but as I recently found out I would get a sixth swarm for free, I set out building a top-bar hive. While the Langstroth hive is a complicated design that requires an expensive centrifugal extractor to harvest the honey, the top-bar hive has sim-plicity at its heart and, while it is less productive, can be made from wood scraps and hand tools, which was exactly what I was doing. This exercise also taught me that hand-sawing wood in a straight line is a skill to be developed, not a given, and my hive was starting to look like the wobbly reflection from a fun-house mirror. The hive constructing process also instilled in me a new respect for the woodworkers of yore who created masterpieces with little more than what they had in my toolbox.

After a few hours passed, I decided it was time to treat the hives for varroa. Varroa mites infest both the bees and larvae of a colony. Oxalic acid does not work against varroa inside brood capped by wax, but is excellent for killing the varroa on adult bees in the hive. In a swarm there is no capped brood and all the varroa are currently on the bees. I mixed the proper amount of acid powder and sugar syrup together and looked inside the closet. Opening the door, a soft light splashed upon the two boxes and surrounding equipment. Though inside each box was a deep darkness, I could hear a soft buzzing and see insect feet and antennae poking through the mesh.

Using a syringe, I took 50 ml of the treatment and dribbled it on the screen of one swarm box. The buzzing timbre changed and increased in volume. A worried thought popped into my head: what if I gave them too much? 50 ml was the maximum amount of treatment, and should only be used on very large swarms. It was hard to tell its size from the outside; the bees hung onto the mesh and I couldn't see anything. Perhaps 50 ml was too much. I got down on a knee and cracked open the lid.

From inside the box I heard a soft thump, which must have been the cluster of bees falling from the mesh to the bottom, but that information didn't have time to register as I was immediately in pain from multiple stings on my face and arms. I jammed the top back on but it was too late; a clutch of bees had escaped. My first reaction was to close the door behind me, but being trapped in a tiny, pitch-black cavity with an unknown number of flying insects stinging me was no solution, so I slipped out as quickly as I could. To my complete horror, around two dozen these frustrated and confused bees escaped with me and began winging aggressively above the cars of the dental patients. The bee closet was separated from the clinic's entrance by only three paces, and to enter the clinic patients had to ring the bell and wait for someone to buzz them in. At the moment the scene was human-free, but very soon I expected someone to appear. Which would be worse: to get attacked by a swarm of bees on your way to a root canal, or after you'd survived one?

Action was my only option. Apologizing to each honey bee in turn, I swiped at the insects flying through the air. Those buzzing against the glass window received as quick a death as possible. I slapped my palms together, crushing one or two, the bee stinging me in its death throes, I in my flailing getting stung more times in the arms and chest, the pain morphing into a strange rippling sensation across my skin. If someone was watching, they might have interpreted it as a madman's shamanic dance to the blood moon. All I felt was desperation.

A flash of movement came from the clinic's window, so I stopped all thrashing and walked away, calmly, towards the garage. The clinic's door swung open with a creaking sound that I had been listening to all day, and an elderly man stepped out. I leaned against the corner of the garage, pretending to study the neighbor's hedge, but my eyes closely followed the old man's paces as he walked towards his car. He took no note of the fifteen or so bees buzzing around, and I held my breath as he fumbled for his car keys and took a far-too-long a look at his receipt. "Please don't sting him," I cried in thought, "please don't sting him, please don't sting him." The disappointed, angry faces of my girlfriend and hoped-to-be-in-laws appeared in my vision, the color intensified by all they had done for me to get these bees in the first place. Now I had let the stinging insects loose on their customers. Yet somehow the bees didn't take any wrath on this old man, and when he was safely in his car, I finally took a breath.

As the car pulled away, I released my mask of calm and began chasing the bees once again, getting stung a handful more times and wondering forlornly what to do about the half-dozen bees that circled high above the cars. Soon another car came down the lane and I paused to look for something next to the fence. Nero, the family's giant black German shepherd, was inside the fence and did not see any reason to stop hunting the bees. He snapped at anything that came near him and even got one or two. "Thanks, Nero," I whispered.

This patient, too, did not react to the loose bees, and walked into the clinic without fanfare. I transformed back into Mr. Hyde. This pattern repeated for the next fifteen minutes: frantic swatting and chasing, dental patients passing, a cracking facade of calm. There was even a second wave when I checked the closet once again and the bees which had left the box but were still stuck in the closet escaped outside, and I was quickly stung four more times. But for whatever reason the bees didn't sting anyone else. Each patient arriving or departing didn't appear to notice the circling insects, instead focused on the fearful appointment ahead of them, or thankful for what they had just survived. In the end, with only a few bees left swirling, I sat down in the garage and began to search for stingers in the pulsating parts of my body: my wrists, my neck, my cheek.

The shadows were growing and it was almost time to bring the bees to their new home. The disappointed faces of my new family drifted away. Innocence in ignorance, I thought. I will never tell them this story.

37

Hive Tool

The hive tool is a beekeeper's best friend. Every beekeeper will have one in the back pocket of his or her work pants, and if it isn't there, you can see probably see the indent from where it usually hangs. Without it, a beekeeper is helpless. Approaching a hive without one is like a baseball player coming to the plate with a roll of wrapping paper.

A simple piece of steel, hour-glass-shaped to fit in the hand, tapered on both edges, often with a small 90° leg on one end, it is an endlessly versatile tool. Hammer? With the flat part you can strike anything. Nail puller? It has a notched hole in the center. Scraper? The sharp, flat edges can take wax off wood or paint off metal. Shoehorn? I've tried it and it works. Spoon? Used to deliver medicines into the hive and honeycomb in my mouth, hopefully not without a good cleaning in between. Backscratcher? Gets to those hard to reach places. Knife? I have heard of a beekeeper pulling it out at the dinner table to cut a steak. Crowbar? Ah, this is its main job, and it is perfect for this purpose.

Inspecting a colony requires a few steps. After a few puffs of smoke to quiet the bees, you must take off the lid, then the supers, before getting into the deep, brood box where the queen hangs out and all the interesting stuff takes place. But lifting the top can be hard—it feels a little stuck—and taking off the super with only your hands can be impossible. The bees often seal every crack and crevice in their hive with propolis: a sticky substance made from plant resin. This also essentially glues the hive together. But shove a hive tool into the seam, lift slightly, and the top super cracks off to reveal the next layer of the colony. Inside the super are nine or ten tightly-packed frames, also glued in with propolis. Fingers on their own are also worthless here, but slipping the tip of the hive tool under the top of the outer frame, the super's edge becomes a fulcrum, and with a small push downward, the frame pops out. With one frame missing, small flicks of the wrist let the hive tool separate the frames, and suddenly the world of the colony is accessible. Archimedes would be pleased.

I received my first hive tool in Texas. It was shiny and new, with part of it painted red so it could easily be spotted in the grass. Over the course of a season, vigorous work beat all other equipment into ruin—gloves developed holes, boots fell apart, suits and veils tore—but the hive tool stayed strong. It lost its shine and the paint chipped off, leaving it an entirely dull gray, but I grew accustomed to its shape, and, if I may say, its spirit. It became an extension of my hand as I sped through one long row of pallets, popping off supers with the crack of splitting wood, the flick of my wrist pushing frames around the box, lifting supers with it still tucked into my palm. When I forgot my hive tool, either back at the shop or at home, the day automatically turned sour. Perhaps someone else had a hive tool that I could borrow, or worse, I would have to make do without one. A flat-head screwdriver is an uncouth solution in a jam, and I have even used a fork to get through a yard with some embarrassment, but without the right tool everything slows down, and the reunion becomes joyous when that familiar piece of metal is back in my hand.

After the start of my commercial beekeeping career, I brought my hive tool everywhere. It sat in the pocket of my passenger door as I drove around the US. When traveling abroad, it was tucked in the top pocket of my pack so if I spied a beehive somewhere and the owner wasn't around, that and a small net veil would allow me to pop inside to see what the bees in this corner of the world looked like. It was also a kind of professional handshake. Once when I had a few days to kill in Oregon before a flight, I knocked on the door of a beekeeper, showed him my hive tool, and spent the next few days camped out in his back yard, scraping boxes for a few bucks an hour.

Barry from North Dakota once showed me his grandfather's hive tool which he still sometimes used, and I vowed that one day I too would pass mine to the next generation. There were points when I lost the tool, sometimes for weeks at a time, but with a careful enough memory recall and thorough searching around the bee yards, it reliably showed up every time.

Until one day in Slovenia. The hive tool that I had developed such a relationship with just disappeared. I only had one yard, and one shop, and didn't believe it could be anywhere other than those two places. Or maybe it could. There had been more than one incident in Texas when we arrived at a yard to find my tool resting on the flatbed, exactly where I had left it while tying down the ropes. One solid bump over that twenty-minute drive could have sent the hive tool forever into the unknown, but luck was on my side those days.

Not so in Slovenia. I still shuffle through the leaves and grasses surrounding my bee yard hoping to kick it loose. Perhaps the tool and I are just on an extended break. I bought a new hive tool, promptly lost that one, and then purchased a third and even a backup fourth. I'm not working with it as much as I did during my commercial days, so at the end of the first season, it still has its paint, and the shine is only muffled. By most means of observation, it looks and feels like my old hive tool. But in my heart, I know it is not.

38

Slovenia Guide

Slovenia is a proud nation of beekeepers. When I first arrived in the country and met Slovenes, I was struck by their high level of knowledge and interest in bees. Everyone I met had an uncle or a grandfather who was a beekeeper, and I would not be surprised if Slovenia has the highest beekeeper-per-capita ratio in the world. This cultural relationship with the bee stems from a few things: a native subspecies (the Carniolan bee, which is the second most-used subspecies in the world), a wealth and variety of nectar-producing plants, and a traditional small-farm system where every family had a beehive or two to provide a sweetener for the diet.

Digging deeper into Slovene apiculture unearths the unique and fertile customs that have developed over time. The Slovenian language has a few interesting examples. One old-time saying for "good luck" translates to, "May your axe land in honey." This refers to someone heading into the woods to chop down a tree for wood, but then coming back with a tree that held a feral bees' nest as well as the bounty of honey within. Another poignant example is the word, "to die." In Slovene you use *umreti* to refer to a human and *poginiti* when speaking of an animal. Traditionally, the only animal with the privilege of sharing the word umreti with humans is the honey bee.

One of my favorite Slovene apicultural traditions is the *panjske končnice*. These are paintings that decorate the fronts of Slovene hives above where the bees enter. The most commonly used hive in America is called the Langstroth, which is like a solitary building that opens from the top. When working with the Langstroth hive, the beekeeper progressively strips away levels until reaching the bottom. The hive typically used in Slovenia—the Anton Žnideršič, or AŽ, hive—is opened from a latched door in the back, like a cupboard, and the frames are taken out one at a time. This allows the hives to be stacked side by side as well as on top of each other, and Slovene beekeepers put these hives, anywhere from two to a hundred, together in a hut called a *čebelnjak*. The bees exit in one direction while the beekeeper does the hive manipulations inside the shed. This method of beekeeping has its technical advantages and disadvantages, but there is no question that a čebelnjak is a more pleasing structure for beekeeper and observer alike. While American hives are often a plain white and tucked away in yards hidden from the public's (and the bee rustler's) eye, the Slovene bee huts are celebratory in nature—beautiful structures that complement a yard or add an elegant dash of humanity to a natural scene.

In keeping with the orderly Slovene ethos, a čebelnjak is also like a small cathedral in which one extols the sublime realm of human-insect cooperation and its ephemeral, sweet output. When I enter a čebelnjak and the bee-scents fill my nose, I feel calm, transported back in time, and sense that a few of the strands connecting me to nature have not fully snapped. Some čebelnjaki also have a bed on top of the hives so one can rest or even sleep in this environment. The hardcore apitherapist will have an oxygen mask with a hose connected to the back of a hive which you can put over your snout and mainline the air directly from the heart of the colony.

The admiration a beekeeper forms with his or her charges on the inside of these houses is translated in a different manner on the outside. Painting the fronts of the hives started sometime in the 1700s as a phylactic symbol: pictures of Mary, Jesus and St. Florijan (the saint of beekeepers and firefighters) were meant to protect the colony and help the harvest. Though beekeepers may not have known this at the time, having a unique painting on each hive also helped the foraging bees know which hive to return to amidst a row of others and probably did help their productivity.

Over time the content of the paintings began to evolve into different themes—around six hundred motifs—including depictions of bible tales, religious imagery, historical stories, and pagan rituals. The most memorable *končnice* are the jokes: a group of devils using an axe grinder to sharpen the tongue of a woman, a pair of neighbors fighting over a cow with the lawyer underneath taking all the milk, a whole series of paintings that lampoon tailors (I'm not sure what they had against tailors in those days, but they are often depicted as being treed by giant snails, implying something about their speed), or two wives taking their husbands away from the poker table while the bachelor sweeps in all the earnings. Women are frequent butts to these jokes, as in those times beekeeping was a male activity, and one can imagine a čebelnjak as a place a beekeeper might flee to as needed—a place where he could tell a few of these jokes to his friends.

My favorite motifs are the simple scenes—a painting of flowers, a farm scene, or the emblematic Slovene setting of a few houses surrounding a church on top of a hill. The one that stands above the rest for me is of a beekeeper sitting next to his čebelnjak with a pipe in his mouth and watching his bees fly. In some versions his kids or family are there with him, in others he is by himself with a glass of wine and a half-carafe on the table next to him. But all versions capture that perfect moment, where the chores are done on a late summer afternoon, and you can sit down and feel pleasantly tired among the marvel of honey bees.

These moments don't last long. Soon you notice that the one weak hive in the corner doesn't seem to be getting any better, that the nectar flow will soon be over, and you worry that the stronger hives may begin to rob from it. Then the sun sets, the pleasant tiredness turns into fatigue, and small reminders come about the endless list of things that will need to be done tomorrow and the week ahead, and these can easily precede thoughts of dirt and greed and politics and human weakness that flood in at the slightest invitation. Yet the serene moment that the painting captures is what we need to covet—to work towards and then enjoy the moments that are within our grasp. When this painting sits over the colony's entrance, the bees don't see a content man with his glass of wine. The bees just see shapes—a sign pointing towards home. But we beekeepers also need our guide.

39

Slovenia Death and Life

2015

The journey to my beehives was almost like traveling back in time. From my 6th floor apartment in Ljubljana, it was just a short drive to get beyond the city's ring road and into villages and farmland. Next I shot into a long, beautiful dale and followed the winding road along a stream, past trim houses festooned with geraniums and carnations, until the landscape opened into a larger valley where the town of Horjul sat snuggly at the foot of south-facing hills. In Horjul I turned north, drove steeply uphill, and followed a road only one-and-a-half vehicles wide and without a guardrail, often with a slow-moving farm tractor chugging around a blind corner, or fragments of fallen rock scattered about the tarmac. When the trees thinned the view was stunning; the Horjul valley, a small forested ridge and then a giant wetland where, legend has it, Jason and the Argonauts slew a dragon. Beyond that the mountain Krim hulks out of the earth. At this height, I finally felt removed from the intensity of microscopic city-life and could take a momentary breath in space and thought.

Once the road stopped climbing I confronted another undeniable Slovene habitat—that no hill should be without a church decorating its top. This church was accompanied by a four-house village, followed by a view of rolling hill-tops, cottages, and old men cutting down hay with scythes. On clear days, the great Julian Alps iced against the northern horizon. My six hives sat on a sliver of land between a quiet road and a hollow that was too steep to mow. On the far side of the road stood a copse of chestnut trees, which flowered in June and provided my bees their main diet: a rich, dark, and delicious honey.

The flip-side to this location was that, at a thirty-minute drive, it wasn't easy for me to just pop over. Also, as I didn't have a car, every trip had to be coordinated with Kati and our competing schedules. I didn't get up there as often as I liked, but my favorite times were when nothing was left of the day, and I could savor the long summer evenings while watching the foragers return from their final trip, eavesdropping on the diurnal creatures quieting down and the nocturnal ones speaking up, and listening to the bells from surrounding hill-top churches chime across the valley to each other. In the end, it would only be a handful of guard bees standing at the entrance watching the deep-purple skies grow even deeper with me.

This first summer beekeeping on my own was a flurry of learning. With all the decisions resting on me alone, I was looking at the hives with different eyes. Also, after spouting for many years the one main lesson I had learned in my travels—that beekeeping is mainly about geography—it finally hit home. Genetics, beekeeping skill, and location are the rungs of the ladder that create a successful season, with the bookends far dominating in importance. In this first season I once again had the strong feeling of the experienced newbie—knowing everything and knowing nothing at the same time.

When starting as a beekeeper, it is vital to have a mentor from your area. No book or internet course will suffice on its own. Keeping bees alive in Minnesota can require a different approach than on similar latitude in Washington State, or in New England (and when heading to a different latitude, or even a different continent, this effect only magnifies). On paper an idea might sound great, and it might work in certain situations, but successful practice, which the local beekeepers have in droves, is what counts.

In Slovenia, I had Janko the Mayor as my mentor. He had helped me with the location, swarms, equipment, advice, and had even let me extract honey in his shop. He went above and beyond what was called for in a mentor. Unfortunately for her, I had to bring Kati along as a translator for every visit. My Slovene was admittedly bad, and Janko did not have much patience to encourage it. He spoke rapidly in a village dialect and whenever I tried to ask or tell him something in Slovene, he would immediately turn to Kati who would translate my poor attempt.

Janko and I came to a crossroads when it came to treating against varroa mites. Varroa is the number one problem for beekeepers around the world: battling against them is the key beekeeper intervention of the year. If you do it right your bees will survive. If not, they will collapse and die. It is often as simple as that. The difficulty comes from trying to kill a smaller bug (the mite) that is on a bigger bug (the bee). The margin of error in the dosage is not large.

Within that context are many shades about how to treat for varroa: it often requires a combination of methods along the treatment spectrum. At one end are the illegal chemicals. Slovenia recently endured a scandal when a local bee supply store was discovered selling Chlorfenvinphos, a highly effective chemical to control varroa, but also a known carcinogen in humans. This was actually a national story in Slovenia and dragged on for a few months, so that most people at least heard about it, and plenty of them cared deeply. As the honey bee could be considered Slovenia's national animal, it made sense, but I was still impressed at the national apiphilia.

The next step in the treatment spectrum are the legal but synthetic chemicals. These, if used in the correct way, won't get into the honey, but can get trapped inside the wax and have mostly unknown synergistic effects with other pesticides brought intentionally or not into the hive. The other problem is that these substances tend to fall on the chemical treadmill: the mites that aren't killed pass their chemical resistance to the next generation. Because mites breed so quickly—a generation every few days—eventually entire mite populations become resistant, and these beekeepers are quickly forced to find a different chemical. Over the decades this treadmill has spun around multiple times, and so far there has always been a back-up plan, but it is never in place until the last minute.

In the third step we cross into "organic" chemicals which are found in nature, but, when used in high concentration, can kill varroa. Formic acid, for example, is found in ants, but can be used as a treatment when released as vapor inside the hive. It can also corrode metal and cause blindness if splashed in the eyes: not exactly an innocent substance.

A fourth step is treatment-free, which is as the name suggests. There are various physical management practices that can help protect hives against varroa, and there are some purists out there who are able to keep bees without putting any of the organic and inorganic chemicals in the hive. These are usually beekeepers with only a few hives and have a good breed of bee, though it is still quite difficult to keep these colonies alive, much less productive.

Janko and I came to the crossroads because he was a step-two person, and I was determined to try step three. I had worked for beekeepers who had used steps one, two and four, but step three made the most sense to me. Even though I didn't have any experience, I read articles, spoke with people, and believed that I could somehow pull it off. The bees had already been treated once that year, and I had heard that colonies could survive a few years before the varroa killed them, so I didn't feel that much pressure. After harvesting the honey, I waited a few weeks and checked the mite levels with a varroa shake. This involves taking a sample of bees, sprinkling them with powdered sugar, and shaking them in a jar until the mites are dislodged and can be counted. The test showed my hives had many mites, and I decided to treat them with oxalic acid. The following week, in spite of my treatment, I discovered that my top-bar was in the final stages of dwindling. I checked the mite levels in the other hives again and saw that they hadn't improved. They might have even been worse.

Summer wasn't exactly the right time of the year to use oxalic acid, so I switched tactics. A few weeks later, I treated them with formic acid, but without the proper application method—doing it correctly required purchasing an extra dispenser and wick for each hive. Instead I found a DIY video on the Internet which said a metal take-away container with a piece of cloth soaked in acid worked just as well. I measured out the acid onto each cloth and left the bees as they were.

When I came back on a cold Saturday in September, the bees looked to be in much worse shape. The formic acid had taken them down a notch, one queen had either died or stopped laying, and I could see bees wearing the small red dots of varroa—a dire sign of infestation. What to do? I had read that more than one of these treatments per year would be harmful to the bees. Was it better to treat them again, or switch to something different? That afternoon I drove an hour to a bee supply store, bought some thyme-based treatment, and drove back. The gray autumn sky and the road climbing the hill no longer held the summer charm I once basked in. I soaked some fabric pads in thyme oil and put them in the hives.

The following weeks I was in Poland and could not shake the dark thoughts of my bees huddled together and fending off voracious varroa. When I returned, two hives had perished. Only two were left and the varroa levels were still high. I called another friend and asked what I could do. He suggested putting oxalic acid in a spray bottle and trying again. That afternoon I drove back in a cold rain and I sat in the car with my head on the steering wheel while waiting for a break in the clouds. When the rain slowed, I jumped out and opened the hives. The bees were clustered together in a small ball, buzzing slightly at the disturbance. Maybe disturbing them in this weather was worse, I suddenly realized, and maybe there was nothing I could do. Even so, action felt better than doing nothing, and I quickly began pulling out combs and spraying both sides, but before I could finish, the rain started again, and I ran back to the car. I put my head on the steering wheel again and felt like crying.

The drive to Horjul at the end of October had a somber feel to it. The window flower boxes had been taken down, gardens lay dormant, and the trees that still did have leaves were a sickly orange-brown. Part of me wanted to let the hives be for the winter, that I might return in the spring with a pleasant surprise of activity, but another part of me wanted the truth: the bees were dead. Their bodies littered the bottoms of the hives and lay scattered in front of the entrances, soon to be eaten by birds and hedgehogs. I tipped over each hive, splattering the comb across the ground. All the experience and years of work had brought me here to Slovenia, all the time, money and effort I had spent this summer to care for these little creatures, all the joy I had felt spending time with them, was destroyed by hubris, lassitude and ideology. Only empty boxes remained. I sat down and looked at the hollow in front of me, devoid of cows, and listened to the church bells ringing maliciously over the far hill.

In the past years, when people asked what I was, I was proud to tell them I was a beekeeper. It was my profession. Though I studied other things in school and had worked at other jobs, my passion was honey bees—working with and writing about them. Sitting on that hill with their deaths laid bare in front of me, my foundations felt weak, my identity thin, my "it will all work out" attitude that I'd kept close in my pocket, for good or for bad, confronting me with its ugly mug. What kind of beekeeper was I if my bees die? How could I tell my friends and family this? How could I admit to Janko that I was wrong?

Looking at the trees and the sky, I thought: I have to. There is no other way. There is nothing to do but pick up and try again. Next year. The church bells will ring next year.

Months passed. That winter I researched varroa treatments and in the spring I bought new colonies, ten of them, doubling down on my fortunes. That summer I let the bees keep all their honey, purchased the right formic acid equipment, and religiously counted mites. In September Kati and I got married, doubling down on my Slovene fortunes as well. As the bees went into that winter, I fed them sugar syrup to bolster their stores. Only eight hives remained, for I had combined two weak ones. It is a beekeeping adage, that it is better to lose the colonies in the fall than over the winter. I felt ready.

What I wasn't prepared for was the extended worry. That January was a frigid one: we had a New Year's snow followed by weeks when temperatures didn't get above freezing. At night, when lying under a pile of blankets in bed, it was difficult imagining those tiny insects spending all their hours inside a small shelter of wood in the deep, unbroken cold.

While bumble bees and other solitary bees hibernate, honey bees do not; they are as awake in the winter as they are in the summer. The queen stops laying eggs in the fall, and a skeleton crew of a few thousand will overwinter. They survive by gathering together in a dense cluster—the colder it is, the more compact they get, sometimes as small and tight as a fist—and they keep the inside of the cluster warm by vibrating their wing muscles. They get the energy to shiver by eating honey. When the bees on the outside of the cluster get cold, they rotate inward and the warm bees take their place. At the very heart of the cluster is the queen, where the temperature is a constant 95°F. throughout the winter. Research has shown that as long as there are enough healthy bees that have access to honey, a colony can survive absurdly low temperatures. A colony once survived twelve hours at -112°F.

Even though I was fairly sure my bees had enough honey, it was hard to imagine their survival as I went about my chilly winter routines: crunching through crusty snow with my dog Pepelka, scraping ice off the windshield, or working in my unheated garage. If the colony didn't have enough bees, an extended period of cold might trap the cluster in one section of the hive and they might freeze to death while mere inches away from a full comb of honey. There was nothing to do but wait.

I distracted myself with activity, perhaps purposely, until the final week of February when one sun-struck afternoon cried for judgment. I packed a jug of sugar syrup and Pepelka in the back of the car and drove to Horjul. It was time to see if the bees had survived.

The drive to Horjul showed the land waking up. The earliest spring flowers began to poke through the forest floor. With an anxious feeling swirling in my gut, the trip seemed to take a long time. I didn't know if I had the heart to take another full loss. A least a few of the hives had to be alive. That would be progress. I thought about a Cali beekeeper named Seth whom I had spilled my story to the previous year. His reply was, "Oh, yeah, I lost all my bees a couple of times. It happens. It sucks."

Coming around the bend, my eyes trained on the hives a few hundred yards away. When I parked, I saw movement in the air. Getting out, approaching the hives from the back, standing to the side, I looked down the row of entrances. Bees flew out of each one.

I let out a yelp of relief. In the back of the car, Pepelka barked.

40

New Zealand Discovery

2005

꙳

The knife-edge of paradise is elusive. Utopia is only a few ticks around the circle from dystopia, and all it takes is a change in the slant of light for all that was once beautiful to suddenly have no meaning. Without the right foundation, there can be no building. Without a building, there is no shelter. Without shelter, it can get very cold.

I had dreamed of New Zealand since a summer-work colleague who had traveled there for a year unloaded upon me the many amazing details of her trip: mountains that scraped the sky, hot-tub-hot rivers, glaciers cascading into the sea, volcanic black sand beaches, caves to raft through, bungee jumping, kayaking, surfing, and multi-day mountain hikes that bring you to seemingly another planet. For my entire freshman year of college, I went through the motions of learning, of being on an intense sport team, of doing homework, of making friends, of going to frat parties, all while day-dreaming of being somewhere far away. Though I can't say I had a bad year, a general dreariness inside told me that it was time wasted, and I wasn't happy there. To be happy, I thought, I needed to go to New Zealand.

The following year I decided to leave school and make my dream happen. Luckily, I had parents who were supportive of this idea, and after another stint of grizzly bear work to save money, I boarded a plane to the South Pacific. I carried a backpack of gear and the phone number of a friend of a friend of a friend who owned a sheep ranch. Stepping off the plane and into the January summer sunlight, six months stretched ahead of me where I could work, live, travel, and enjoy.

Fast-forward a few weeks and the dream had unexpectedly soured. I had worked on the sheep farm for a while, mustering and wrestling those dumb beasts. I had bought a clunker car, drove about, and visited the places a traveler visits. Everything was fun and nice, but the feeling of sadness that had troubled me during the previous year persisted. Though masked, it transformed into a slow and surprising realization that perhaps New Zealand itself was not the cure.

I moved on to Golden Bay, the northern tip of the South Island. The town of Takaka was everything I was searching for in life: a small, off-beat hippie town sandwiched between mountains and ocean within easy reach of a handful of national parks. People were extremely friendly. There was a tiny movie theater with beanbags in the front row, and it had the best bar I (still) have ever been to.

But the slant of light wasn't right. Though I had all the freedom in the world—adequate funds, a car, and no plan for the following five months—I would wake up in the morning without any energy or idea of what to do with myself. I could go on a hike and look at a nice natural monument, but, at the end of the day, I would be in exactly the same place. I could join that table of backpackers across the room nursing their hangovers with a joint and then spend the rest of the day chasing that capricious dragon of inebriation until some nocturnal peak was reached and came crashing down with sleep, only for the hunt to be kicked off once again in the morning. Every hostel in New Zealand—and there were a lot of hostels—had that table of hedonists, and it seemed possible to spend one's travels moving from table to table, up and down the coast. That wasn't what I wanted from this trip either.

Indecision held me in the Takaka hostel for nearly a week until one morning when I threw my stuff into the car and drove away. After only two miles I pulled onto a gravel track that led down to a rocky riverbed. I walked to the shadow of the bridge and laid down underneath it.

I laid there for the rest of the morning and then the whole afternoon. I didn't feel like I could go any further, nor did I feel like I could go back. At one point I went to the car and got my camping pad so I wasn't lying directly on the rocks as well as a bottle of water and some crackers before returning to my spot. I listened to river flowing as well as the

249

clunk-da-clunk-da-clunk of cars passing on the bridge overhead while feeling aghast at the void of free will open in front of me. I buried my face in the sand and cried. I felt completely lost.

The feelings were intense and difficult to analyze. Despite the pure luck in my life station, the comfort in which I was raised, the generous love of my family, I felt unhappy. Despite my day-dreaming of the previous year, New Zealand did not cure it. Why not? Why did I think it would? Could true happiness ever be found? Is it something that is chased and caught? Or is it a different thing all together? Does it need to be kindled? What did I want out of this trip anyway? Did I want to go back to university? If not, what would I do after this trip? If so, what would I do after university? What does one do with life? What is a passion? Do you just pick something? Or do you know it when you feel it?

Afternoon turned into evening, evening turned into night. With the exit of the sun, the number of cars slowed overhead, but the river kept me company, as a river always will—constantly narrating the story of raindrops and mountain streams, of fish and fowl that use it: always the same yet ever-changing.

Eventually I slept. I dreamt vivid, intense dreams. I woke to a cool, dawn light and a couple of ducks eying my presence with suspicion. The night passed as it normally did, and I was faced with another day.

I hadn't yet answered all the questions that had confronted me, but I sat with them head-on for long enough that they shied away. Their full force was no longer overpowering. My thoughts were beginning to coalesce.

You can do something with yourself, or you can float along. Life needs a goal. Without one, it is easy to stray. What did I like? Traveling was high on the list—tasting new foods, meeting people who weren't like me, surrounding myself with the unknown, taking adventure head-on. Those all checked my boxes. But, as I came to realize, traveling on its own could be hollow: see the famous thing, take a picture of it, eat at a manufactured "traditional" restaurant, and then get drunk with other tourists. I needed to go deeper. I liked spending time with the ranchers on the sheep farm. I wanted to put myself in foreign places for longer periods of time where I could learn from the locals, and, by the end of it, say that I had at least tasted the culture. But how does one make a living doing that?

What else did I like? Animals. I loved animals of all stripes and was fascinated with how humans and animals interacted. Over thousands of years, we humans have built relationships with certain species so now that in some cases they benefit from us as much as we do from them. How could one work with animals? Conservation, science, farming, veterinary medicine, animal training. In which of these could I actually work with animals, not just have them as numbers on a screen? And how could I combine these two interests—traveling and working with animals?

Morning turned to afternoon. I sat up. The answers I'd built were still only vague shapes, but I felt satisfied enough that I could push forward. This investigation under the bridge had been dark and frightening, but I had pushed through a barrier. Plus, I was out of water and crackers, and hunger had caught up to me. I stuffed my sleeping pad into the trunk of my car and drove back into town.

I spied a parking spot on the main street and slid the old car into it. Every time I started that car, I vaguely wondered if it would it make it to the end of the drive, or if it would conk out and take my $400 with it. The hot sun beat down, and I felt dehydrated. First I would put something in my stomach, then I would push out of this town. Though I liked Takaka, it was time for a change of scenery. I didn't know what the next step would be, but I felt sure I would know when it hit me.

Walking towards the restaurant, I passed a building which seemed to be a bureaucratic office, like a DMV or town register, and in the window I saw a piece of paper taped to the glass that read, "Honey for Sale." I continued past it, but then I stopped. I went back and looked at the sign again. "Honey for Sale" with a picture of a cartoon bee below it.

Honey bees.

Beekeeping.

Now there, I thought to myself, is a curious idea.

I walked inside the office, and a bespectacled woman looked up from her computer. She said, "Can I help you?"

"Yes," I replied. "Can you give me the phone number of the beekeeper in town?"

MUCH APPRECIATION TO:

Joe Graham, for the encouragement in writing and giving my travels an objective.

Danny and Laura Weaver, for the first steps in this journey, and the friendship along the way.

John Kefuss, the super connector!

Larry Connor and Randy Kim, for bringing this collection to life.

My lovely aunts and uncles: Elaine, Lorie, Tim, and David.

Kati, my beauty of a wife, my inspiration.

Meli and Miha, for helping add a happy back third to this story.

My wonderful family, especially my mother, for her editing and advice on all my writing.

All beekeepers whom I worked with, hosted me, and passed on their knowledge.

Everyone who has given a ride, meal, or shown kindness to a traveler.

William Blomstedt was born in Washington State and was raised in Western Massachusetts. He graduated from Dartmouth College with a degree in geography and biology and received a masters in geographical information science from the University of Edinburgh. Between degrees he worked as a beekeeper and queen breeder around the globe and wrote dozens of articles for the *American Bee Journal*. He now lives in Ljubljana, Slovenia with his wife, dog, hedgehog, and bees.